Conscious Healing

Book One on the Regenetics Method

Sol Luckman

Conscious Healing: Book One on the Regenetics Method

Booklocker Publishing
PO Box 2399, Bangor, ME 04402-2399
http://www.booklocker.com
10-Digit ISBN: 1-59113-843-4
13-Digit ISBN: 978-1-59113-843-3
First Edition printed in the United States of America.

Library of Congress Control Number: 2005910209
Library of Congress, Cataloging in Publication Division
101 Independence Avenue, SE, Washington, DC 20540-4320

For those with ears to hear
& our little heron from Tula

CONTENTS

LIST OF ILLUSTRATIONS

INTRODUCTION

This is a truly exciting time to be alive. As a species, judging by our "postmodern" art and "subquantum" science, we are learning just how completely we create our own reality. Central to this evolution of human consciousness is a growing appreciation of the many ways we (collectively and individually) create ourselves. Literally. DNA is the alphabet we divinely endowed biological beings use to compose our existence.

Revolutionary new research in "wave-genetics" reveals DNA can be activated—noninvasively—by radio and light waves keyed to human language frequencies. Studies by cell biologists further demonstrate that the genetic code can be stimulated through human consciousness—specifically, the unity consciousness associated with unconditional love—to heal not only the mind and spirit but the body as well. Benefits of DNA activation can range from allergy relief and increased energy to better relationships and even renewed life purpose. Since DNA regulates all physical, mental, emotional and spiritual aspects of our being, the possibilities are endless!

In the words of bestselling author and leading health researcher Dr. Leonard Horowitz, DNA with its "stunning ability ... to function as a receiver and transmitter of ... the Divine Cosmic Song" represents "far more than a static blueprint for body building." DNA, which Horowitz calls the "Sacred Spiral," is the "ideal super conductor, and micro-antennae, designed to perfection beyond the reach of the wildest imagination, for physical re-spiritualization." DNA constitutes the "central processing station for human electricity and evolutionary destiny. If 'knowledge is power,' revealing [DNA's] secrets is the key to personal empowerment, spiritual evolution, and even planetary salvation."

Taken together, such pioneering, relatively unknown, and often suppressed genetic research reveals an astonishing wealth of potential: to "reset" bioenergetic systems damaged by trauma and toxicity, to stimulate bioenergy and creativity, even to "switch on" untapped capabilities in the human brain as steps toward unity consciousness and its corresponding evolved biology. Thanks to a holistic technique for DNA activation we at the Phoenix Center call the Regenetics Method, an affordable, effective means is now available to "potentiate" one's entire being.

Potentiation Electromagnetic Repatterning, a central focus of this book, is the first of three integrated DNA activations that make up the Regenetics Method. Regenetics is a unique synthesis of ideas in action designed to improve lives in numerous ways, tangible and subtle. It is my intent that your own life will be improved even as you thoughtfully consider the concepts presented herein. Additional information on the second and third phases of the Regenetics Method, Articulation Bioenergy Enhancement and Elucidation Triune Activation, is available online at http://www.phoenixregenetics.org and http://www.potentiation.net.

This text is divided into two principle parts, the first reflecting the "micro" aspect of Regenetics, the second providing a "macro" perspective on this method in relation to human evolution. In the first part, "Textual Healing with Potentiation Electromagnetic Repatterning: Introducing the Art & Science of the Regenetics Method," I share the story of my nearly eight-year chronic illness, with an emphasis on the development of Potentiation and how I used this DNA activation to heal myself.

Part II, "Sacred Cosmology, Sacred Biology: The Regenetics Method & the Evolution of Consciousness," complements Part I with a macrocosmic presentation of Regenetics in the greater context of the evolution of consciousness. Here I draw on the work of many outstanding thinkers from a variety of orientations who share the belief in a purpose and direction to human life—that as a species we are evolving in a specific manner on a prescribed timeline. It is my intention that Part II will stimulate your curiosity about human evolution in general, while inspiring you to explore avenues such as the Regenetics Method for fully actualizing your own unique potential.

In addition to Parts I and II, I have included three substantial Appendices as educational resources. Appendix A provides wide-ranging Testimonials from individuals who have experienced Potentiation. Appendix B contains detailed answers to Frequently Asked Questions about Potentiation and the Regenetics Method. Appendix C is a representative Electromagnetic Schematic of the first of twelve "Electromagnetic Groups" encountered during the development of the Regenetics Method as described in Chapter Four.

Additionally, I have provided an extensive Index as well as a comprehensive Glossary of Terms derived from various disciplines that may be new to the reader or that I employ in specialized ways. I invite you to use this

Glossary as a reference and also to read it in its entirety as a "journey in consciousness." Finally, a complete Bibliography is included to assist those who wish to explore the science and philosophy behind Regenetics in greater depth.

Many of the concepts behind Potentiation Electromagnetic Repatterning and the Regenetics Method outlined in this book may strike the reader as "cutting-edge." While they may indeed appear that way in this day and age, most of them are also, paradoxically, extremely old. They stem from time-honored practices rooted in the curative power of prayer, shamanic medicine, and specifically the balanced use of *sound* and *intention* to heal in ways that can seem miraculous to many Westerners. I will share some fascinating scientific research that substantiates these phenomena. But before proceeding, allow me to call your attention to the old adage of how a new truth typically comes to be accepted.

"All truth passes through three stages," wrote Arthur Schopenhauer. "First, it is ridiculed. Second, it is violently opposed. Third, it is accepted as being self-evident." In a similar vein, Albert Einstein once said, "If at first an idea isn't absurd, there's no hope for it." I offer that the Regenetics Method (and modalities based on similar principles) represents one such "absurdly profound" truth that will eventually become self-evident. Thank you for your interest in this work and willingness to expand—perhaps—your vision of who you are and what is humanly possible.

—Sol Luckman
Co-founder, The Phoenix Center for Regenetics

Facilitating conscious personal mastery as a bio-spiritual healing path through integrated DNA activation.
Editor, *DNA Monthly*
Your free *online resource for cutting-edge news about who you truly are.*
http://www.phoenixregenetics.org
http://www.potentiation.net
December 2005

NOTE ON TERMINOLOGY

The following text, like the Regenetics Method, is a synthesis of concepts from many disciplines running the gamut from hard science to speculative cosmology. Such a comprehensive approach, while demonstrating the considerable scope of Regenetics, is not without presenting certain difficulties for some lay readers— particularly at the level of terminology.

Time and again, my multidisciplinary research has revealed that the numerous fields of scientific and philosophical inquiry have produced different terms for describing the same phenomena. While this tends to validate the phenomena themselves as essential to human experience, confusion can result unless we understand that many of the words and phrases employed by the various disciplines are, for practical purposes, synonyms. Wherever appropriate, I have provided definitions in the Glossary for such cross-referencing terms that highlight both their similarities and nuances.

Two key examples should suffice to call attention to this dynamic and facilitate understanding. The following terms for the apparently dormant and unused portion of DNA are, for the purposes of our discussion, virtually synonymous: "junk" DNA, "jumping DNA," potential DNA, introns, and transposons. This subject is covered in detail in Part I.

Similarly, as elaborated in Part II, torsion radiation or energy is simply a scientific way of conceptualizing unconditional love. Both originate from Galactic Center (also referred to as Source, Tula, and the Healing or Central Sun) as the "tone" of Ge, which differentiates into spiral standing waves of sound (radio waves or phonons) and intention (light waves or photons). Other words and phrases used to describe aspects of torsion energy or unconditional love include: Silent Stillness, aether, universal creative consciousness, thought, tachyons, scalar waves, life-wave, orgone energy, chi, prana, *and* kundalini.

"In the order of healing, it is human consciousness that first must change."

—Ken Carey, *Return of the Bird Tribes*

Conscious Healing

• PART I •
TEXTUAL HEALING WITH POTENTIATION ELECTROMAGNETIC REPATTERNING:
INTRODUCING THE ART & SCIENCE OF THE REGENETICS METHOD

1
Nonlocalized Mind & Era III Medicine

One of many inspirational figures behind Potentiation Electromagnetic Repatterning and the Regenetics Method is Dr. Larry Dossey. The reader may be familiar with his bestselling book *Healing Words,* an account of the therapeutic effects of prayer substantiated by numerous scientific studies performed at institutions such as Harvard and Stanford. In *Reinventing Medicine: Beyond Mind-body to a New Era of Healing,* Dr. Dossey reiterates:

> Many studies reveal that healing can be achieved at a distance by directing loving and compassionate thoughts, intentions, and prayers to others, who may even be unaware these efforts are being extended to them. These findings reveal the ability of some part of our mind or consciousness to escape its confinement to the brain and body and to act anywhere, regardless of distance.

An important point emerges from this groundbreaking consciousness research: there appears to be no single "correct" type of prayer. "These studies clearly show that *healing intention* is a general term," Dossey emphasizes. "It can be secular or religious; it may or may not involve prayer."

Christians praying to their God for healing, for example, were no more or less successful than Muslims or Jews praying to theirs. So statistically eye-opening were these studies many hospitals now offer nondenominational prayer for patients undergoing life-threatening surgeries. Survival rate and recovery speed are enhanced beyond any doubt by these noninvasive intercessions that have the added merit of being cost-effective. Since the publication of *Healing Words*, a variety of additional studies on prayer and healing have been performed, including a double-blind analysis performed at UCSF-California Pacific Medical Center that showed positive effects of prayer on patients with advanced AIDS.

Active prayer is a method of focusing intention that validates whatever one is praying for as having already been granted.

Other research on the healing power of prayer suggests that a major determining factor of success or failure is the level of *nonattachment* of the pray-er. Between 1975 and 1993 the Spindrift Foundation performed hundreds of thousands of tests to assess the effectiveness of directed prayer (i.e., focused on a specific outcome) versus non-directed prayer (in which only what is best for the person is requested). Both directed and non-directed prayer worked better for the control group for whom no prayers were known to be said, but non-directed prayer showed a significantly higher success rate than directed prayer.

In *The Isaiah Effect* bestselling author Gregg Braden takes the practical applications of prayer a step further. Basing his claims on his reading of one of the

Dead Sea Scrolls known as the Isaiah Scroll, Braden describes how the Essenes from the time of Christ employed a type of prayer designed to affect, and effect, quantum outcomes by literally changing the pray-er's picture of reality. This form of "active prayer," to which I will return in Part II, is a method of focusing intention that validates whatever one is praying for as having already been granted.

"Rather than creating or imposing change upon our world," theorizes Braden, "perhaps it is our ability to change our focus that was the ancient key suggested by the masters of passive change in history" such as Buddha, Gandhi, and Jesus. "Quantum physics suggests that by redirecting our focus—where we place our attention—*we bring a new course of events into focus* while at the same time releasing an existing course of events that may no longer serve us." Author John English, whose novel *The Shift: An Awakening* won the Coalition of Visionary Resources Book of the Year Award in 2004, speaks in similarly compelling terms about the powerful human ability to "dream a new world into being."

In *Reinventing Medicine* Dossey, the former chief of staff at a major Dallas hospital, examines allopathic approaches to healing in light of the principle of "nonlocality" often discussed in relation to quantum physics. Putting modern medicine in quantum perspective, Dossey admits that we "are facing a 'constitutional crisis' in medicine—a crisis over our *own* constitution, the nature of our mind and its relationship to our physical body." To help explain this "constitutional crisis," and to assist humanity in transitioning beyond it, Dossey outlines three eras in the history of Western medicine. While these eras are by no means mutually exclusive, each has a dominant, defining focus.

The first era began in the 17ᵗʰ Century with Cartesian thinking and was characterized by a mechanistic view of the body. Era I medicine looks at the human body more or less as a machine that can be manipulated. In this rather primitive medical model, there is no place for mind or consciousness—and certainly none for "soul" or "spirit." Surgery and vaccines are both applications of Era I medicine.

In the 19ᵗʰ Century, according to Dossey, Era I gave way to Era II with the acknowledgement of the so-called placebo effect. Era II saw the birth of psychoanalysis and psychiatry and is characterized by mind-body approaches to healing. Era II medicine is based on the observation that your mind and body are intimately connected such that *your* consciousness can remedy *your* physiology in provable ways. This is the "power of positive thinking," as Norman Vincent Peale phrased it. Era II techniques continue to play an important role in today's medical paradigm.

As a global culture we are now in the process of greatly expanding that paradigm with what Dossey refers to as Era III medicine, also called "nonlocal." The hallmark of Era III medicine is the "nonlocalized mind," meaning the universal Mind that has also been called unity, Christ, Buddhic and even God consciousness. Physicists sometimes conceptualize nonlocalized mind as the "Unified Field," psychologists often refer to it (following Carl Jung) as the "Ground of Being," while many spiritualists speak of "Source," to borrow a term popularized by famed psychic and healer Edgar Cayce in his remarkable readings.

The term *nonlocal* is particularly relevant to this discussion because of its derivation from science. Physicist David Bohm, one of the founders of the holographic model of reality, has used the phrase "quantum potential" to refer to the nonlocal point in space where space ceases to exist and two electrons, for instance, can occupy the same coordinates. Nonlocalized mind has been variously described, but simply put, it is the Supreme Consciousness of which we are all facets—regardless of whether we choose to acknowledge our interconnectedness.

Nonlocalized mind has been variously described, but simply put, it is the Supreme Consciousness of which we are all facets—regardless of whether we choose to acknowledge our interconnectedness.

The fundamental notion behind Era III medicine, very evident in the writings of Braden and English, is that the human mind can operate *outside* the confines of the physical body and positively impact other people, animals, and even the environment. Some may be conditioned to believe this is impossible. Others may be aware of such studies as Princeton Engineering Anomalies Research (PEAR) that present solid, empirical evidence of the ability of human consciousness to change physical reality, including the mind's capacity to affect the outcome of random-number generators and alter the rate of radiation emissions as measured by a Geiger counter.

I offer this first-person narrative of the development of Potentiation Electromagnetic Repatterning to members of both these groups and all others willing to open their hearts and minds to the essential truths that underwrite the Regenetics Method—

truths that can be productively applied in many areas (personal and professional) besides DNA activation. In the following pages, I will focus my observations on the positive impact of nonlocalized mind on human beings, but the majority of the concepts I introduce should be easily understood as applying to the world at large.

2
Autoimmunity & Energy Clearing's Brave New World

Before further exploring the pivotal concept of Era III medicine, nonlocalized mind, a word or two about my own background is in order. I grew up in a small Southern town, where I excelled athletically and academically. I was quarterback as well as valedictorian and ended up winning a prestigious college scholarship. I was offered the chance to play Division I football—which I declined because I already had academic funding. I went on to graduate at the top of my scholarship class, win a Fulbright teaching award, and receive an Ivy League doctoral-candidate fellowship followed by two national research grants in the humanities.

My most remarkable characteristic as a younger man was an intense passion to experience life fully. The implications of this passion only dawned on me after living "fully" came to include suffering disease and descending into a "dark night of the soul" after the onset of a mysterious, debilitating illness in 1996. At that time I was working on a Ph.D. in literature. This is significant because I tend to approach the Regenetics Method from a "literary" perspective, as the titles of this section and chapter suggest. I will elaborate momentarily.

To make a very long story short, at twenty-seven life inexplicably came crashing down. One day I was exercising three hours at a stretch, able to eat and drink whatever I pleased. The next I was gripped by a mysterious illness that, one by one, took away the foods, drinks and sports I loved, even—in the insidious way chronic illness has of stripping you clean—many people I loved.

Despite a string of "negative" medical tests, I lay in bed night after night terrified I was dying. In addition to debilitating allergies and exhaustion, I suffered from approximately thirty seemingly unrelated symptoms, including back pain, hypoglycemia, receding gums, skin rashes, shortness of breath, and chemical sensitivities. In an effort to halt my deterioration, I took nearly every supplement on the market. I received regular intravenous chelation. I experimented with ozone and infrared saunas. I went on parasite cleanses, special diets for Candida. I tried reiki, acupuncture, homeopathy, biofeedback, magnets, "zappers." I underwent EMDR, hypnosis, radionics, even "psychic surgery." But after trying practically everything and spending a fortune, I was sicker than ever and getting worse.

Eventually, my health deteriorated to where I could only eat meat and vegetables. At one point my white blood cell count was alarmingly low. I was never officially diagnosed with anything but the medical profession's catchall for baffling conditions—"depression"—although I am now certain my disease was of a serious autoimmune nature precipitated by hepatitis and yellow fever vaccines I received before traveling to South America for dissertation research in 1995. Even at the time of my diagnosis, I felt deeply that depression was the result not the cause of whatever was degenerating my once athletic body. But I dutifully popped my pills until I nearly died of an adverse reaction. Growing desperate, with little left to lose, I headed into "alternative" territory seeking solutions.

In terms of understanding what had gone haywire in me, my biggest breakthrough came when I grasped the role vaccines play in creating autoimmunity. For a sobering look at the potentially disastrous consequences of vaccines, I recommend Leonard Horowitz's *Emerging Viruses: AIDS & Ebola—Nature, Accident or Intentional?* In this eye-opening bestseller, Harvard-trained Dr. Horowitz persuasively argues that vaccines are the root cause of a long list of autoimmune diseases, including AIDS. Following the discovery of simian 40 retrovirus (sometimes referred to as "monkey AIDS") in polio vaccines, many other researchers, among them dozens of biologists and medical doctors, have reached similar conclusions.

After a year spent testing Horowitz's ideas, I concluded that immune-wrecking retroviruses can penetrate the bloodstream via "immunizations" and alter one's genetic code, potentially sabotaging health under a myriad of creative diagnoses such as "fibromyalgia," "chronic fatigue," and "multiple chemical sensitivity."

This may strike anyone who accepts the official line that vaccines are safe and effective as unbelievable. But after a year spent testing Horowitz's ideas at the energetic level, I concluded that immune-wrecking retroviruses can penetrate the bloodstream via "immunizations" and alter one's genetic code, potentially sabotaging health under a myriad of creative diagnoses such as "fibromyalgia," "chronic fatigue," and "multiple chemical sensitivity." Many thousands of unsuspecting people have died or been permanently handicapped following adverse reactions to vaccines. Even the medical establishment recently linked certain childhood vaccines to autism.

A major contributing factor to many, if not all, autoimmune conditions is genetic damage through invasive factors such as vaccines compounded by cellular toxicity. I contend that cells collect and hold toxicity for the purpose of slowing down the many mutant pathogens, such as simian 40 retrovirus, released in the organism under the radar of the immune system by vaccines. The body knows that toxic substances—heavy metals and pesticides, for instance—are not only poisonous to the host, but also to pathogens. Such a Catch-22 can lead to environmental illness and immunological breakdown in which the body starts attacking its own toxic cells, but it may be the only choice a biosystem operating with damaged DNA has.

Many people are led to believe that since they have an autoimmune disorder or disease, they are more toxic *because* of their chemical, environmental or nutritional sensitivities. Another way of saying this is that it is commonly assumed the body becomes more toxic in autoimmune states because it cannot or does not know how to detoxify. Based on my research and personal experience of genetic collapse, however, it appears that autoimmunity is induced by foreign genetic invaders (which can include genetically modified foods) that negatively reprogram DNA by utilizing the body's RNA transcription process, instructing the body to replicate artificial codes inside cells. In other words, once DNA is reprogrammed, it literally has the ability to grow new pathogenic—perhaps "pathogenetic" would be a better word—cellular cultures.

According to Horowitz and many other researchers, vaccine-induced pathogens, in addition to simian 40 retrovirus, can include prions, mycoplasmas, mouse parotid tumor tissue, bovine lymphotropic virus, feline leukemia virus, Epstein-Barr virus, and Rous sarcoma virus—to name only a few. When these are "uploaded" into the genetic code using the reverse transcriptase ("backward writing") enzyme, any number of autoimmune conditions can result—from lupus to leukemia, depending on the individual's constitution and lifestyle and the number and type of vaccines received.

The body, in its wisdom, realizes it has been fundamentally altered, but like a computer it must carry out the codes in its reprogrammed DNA. This can lead to a degenerative defense response as the body accumulates more and more toxicity in an attempt to "short-circuit" the foreign pathogens being grown like weeds in the cells. The body simply uses what is available from the environment in its biological war against itself.

The body, in its wisdom, realizes it has been fundamentally altered, but like a computer it must carry out the codes in its reprogrammed DNA. Over time, this can lead to a degenerative defense response as the body accumulates more and more toxicity in an attempt to "short-circuit" the foreign pathogens being grown like weeds in the cells. The body simply uses what is available from the environment in its biological war against itself.

What often happens with Candida following such genetic damage is very telling. There is nothing inherently wrong with Candida. In a properly functioning body, *Candida albicans* keeps tissues healthy by scavenging potentially harmful microorganisms and toxins. Candida only gets out of control when the body tries to defend itself from some other invasion, usually of a genetic nature. This cycle is nearly impossible to halt without interceding "ener-genetically" because the problem is in the DNA, which unless directed to resume normal biological operations, continues a vicious cycle of replicating its mutated codes, then futilely trying to clean up microorganism overgrowth with more overgrowth!

Sensitivities and allergies result when the body is so occupied in the war going on at the level of the cells and immune system it cannot handle or take on additional foreign substances. In many cases, microorganism populations are so out of balance they actually consume the host's food and produce additional toxic waste, such as fungal mycotoxins, inside and outside cells—further exacerbating an already genetically entrenched state of autoimmunity.

In the second year of my illness, in consultation with a holistic doctor, I became convinced mercury poisoning was also a factor deranging my immune system. After reading an enormous amount of material on the controversial subject of mercury and other heavy metals in dentistry, I decided to undergo the painful process of having my amalgam fillings removed following a protocol similar to one developed by Dr. Hal Huggins. Actually, I ended up going through this protocol *twice*, after my first dentist made a mistake and replaced my mercury with barium and other metals![1]

For all the trauma it caused my mouth (and wallet), getting my dental work redone and removing such a toxic load of heavy metals from my system sparked a temporary "spontaneous remission." I was immediately almost back to my old self. I went from being unable to eat carbohydrates or drink alcohol, before removal of my amalgams, to getting up out of the dental chair after my fourth and final appointment and being able to enjoy pizza and beer that afternoon! I had no Candida or leaky gut reaction whatsoever. To one who had been allergic to nearly everything, it was a miracle. I was able to resume my normal routine for about five months—until I began to lose ground again.

This time I rapidly went downhill. In desperation, I took a leave of absence from graduate school and moved to New Mexico to study qigong. Qigong is an ancient Chinese technique of energy healing related to tai chi. I studied with a master who had cured himself of chronic fatigue syndrome (CFIDS) while also in his twenties. I practiced at least three hours a day for a year while receiving weekly acupuncture treatments and taking copious quantities of Chinese herbs.

---

[1] As it turned out, much of the material I read on mercury cross-referenced the vaccine issue. "We are changing our genetic code through vaccination," write health researchers Robert and Kerrie Broe, to cite one example. In the future, the Broes insist, basing their position on decades of in-depth research, it will be acknowledged that two of the "biggest crimes against humanity were *vaccines* and *mercury dental fillings*."

This probably saved my life and certainly got me back on my feet. I took a teaching job at a preparatory school and was actually strong enough to go trekking around in the woods with a heavy backpack. But I was still having terrible food reactions. And if I went more than a couple days without my intensive regimen of qigong, I started to re-experience old symptoms that included involuntary muscle spasms, tingling in my extremities, facial neuralgia, and other frightening neurological sensations. At various points during my illness, I was convinced I had multiple sclerosis or Parkinson disease.

Then of all foolhardy things, I accepted a teaching position at an international school. During my first and only year, I developed back-to-back abscessed teeth that required antibiotics. This was the last straw. The antibiotics wrecked my fragile biological terrain (see Glossary) and I was down for the count. I slept fifteen hours a day, had to quit my job, and went from an already severely restricted diet to being unable to season my meat and vegetables because of crippling allergic reactions. I once quipped during that nightmarish period after returning to the United States with my tail between my legs that I could eat practically anything—as long as it was not food.

It was at this point, when hope was failing and I suspected I was dying, that I stumbled on the brave new world of energy clearing. I am specifically referring to NAET®, Nambudripad's Allergy Elimination Technique, and an offshoot of this therapy called BioSET™, developed by one of Dr. Nambudripad's students, a chiropractor named Ellen Cutler.

As soon as I started receiving NAET® and BioSET™ treatments, I noticed some positive physical shifts. My food allergies temporarily subsided, although they never disappeared entirely, and I experienced some much-needed detoxification. The shifts were so immediate and palpable I found myself considering the possibility of using these modalities to heal my genetic damage, detoxify my cells, and rebuild my deteriorated tissues.

NAET® derives in part from the homeopathic discovery that energy signatures can be imprinted in small glass vials using an electro-acupuncture device. For example, one can place the energy signature (an electromagnetic frequency the body will recognize) of an allergen such as sugar in a vial containing pure water and a drop of alcohol. The immune system's response to the vial is identical, for practical purposes, to its reaction to sugar. Although their cause is never adequately explained, allergies are seen in NAET® as chemical, environmental or nutritional sensitivities that tend to derange the immune system, contributing to a variety of chronic ailments.

The patient then holds the vial with the allergen's energy signature while the practitioner performs acupressure along the spine designed to initiate a "clearing" using the nervous and Eastern meridian systems (see Glossary). The basic idea, similar to that of acupuncture, is to eliminate "blockages" that keep life force or bioenergy from flowing properly through the body. In theory, clearings retrain the body, specifically the immune system, to accept substances formerly rejected as allergens. The popularity of NAET® even among some members of the allopathic community attests to the fact it can produce measurable benefits.

BioSET™ expanded on NAET® by recognizing that if it is possible to clear with one vial at a time, it should be possible to clear using multiple vials. One can clear sugar allergies with *Candida albicans*, which can feed on sugar, and even add vials that represent the pancreatic system, since insulin has a close relationship with sugar. Theoretically, it is even possible to clear heavy metals, viruses and other pathogens that might be impairing pancreatic function. BioSET™ has evolved to such a level of complexity that instead of vials, many practitioners now employ computers for clearings with specialized software and equipment designed to introduce multiple combinations of homeopathic frequencies to the patient.

Initially, I was tremendously encouraged by this approach—especially after I saw some of my severe allergic patterns improve. I ended up pestering my practitioner until she trained me in her own version of BioSET™ and I began making my living with this therapy. I did this for a little over a year, during which I continued to receive treatments from my teacher, before I grew frustrated at my lack of progress and started treating myself.

In order to "reset" our bioenergy blueprint in a way that will not only "take" but also "hold," we must go directly to the source of the electromagnetic malfunction in our genetic code. Only in this manner can we reestablish the energetic harmony and coherence necessary for sustained wellbeing. I concluded that in order to do this, it is necessary to employ sound along with intention to activate the self-healing mechanism in the apparently unused portion of DNA.

In total, I received approximately seventy NAET® and BioSET™ treatments. Doing the math, 70 × $75 at the going rate, I received over $5,000 in treatments. But if anything, after a brief plateau, I was going downhill once again. I was becoming more and more fatigued, losing the foods I had partially gotten back, and even experiencing a variety of new symptoms.

Traditional energy clearings work by way of the nervous and meridian systems. But geneticists have begun to refer to DNA, not the nervous system, as our "biocomputer." In order to "reset" our bioenergy blueprint in a way that will not only "take" but also "hold," we must go directly to the source of the electromagnetic malfunction in our genetic code. Only in this manner can we reestablish the energetic harmony and coherence necessary for sustained wellbeing. Ultimately, I concluded that in order to do this, it is necessary to employ *sound* along with *intention* to activate the self-healing mechanism in the apparently unused portion of DNA. But first, it was necessary to understand the critical role played by the body's electromagnetic or auric fields in creating disease and maintaining health.

3
The Electromagnetic Fields: Our Bioenergy Blueprint

My last several months working with an offshoot of BioSET™, I began intuitively receiving a tremendous amount of information. At this point I was inspired to read a book nearly every other day on biology, chemistry, physics, genetics, new science, energy medicine, or esoterics.[2] A host of interrelated ideas came to me all at once and I began to substantiate them through muscle testing.

The science of muscle testing (kinesiology) employs muscle-response (strong or weak) tests to determine allergies, emotional blockages, and even the truth or falsehood of given statements. Since its invention in the 1960s, kinesiology has become popular among both alternative and mainstream healthcare professionals around the world. For those unfamiliar with the many applications of kinesiological testing, I recommend *Power vs. Force: The Hidden Determinants of Human Behavior*, by Dr. David Hawkins. This famous text, praised by Mother Teresa among others, provides a thought-provoking introduction to the fascinating field of kinesiology. For present purposes, it is simply necessary to mention that muscle testing, properly utilized, can be a

---

[2] A number of these books are listed in the Bibliography.

powerful tool for gathering and evaluating information that has been empirically validated on numerous occasions.

My partner Leigh assisted me throughout the development of the Regenetics Method. Without her keen insight and unwavering support, this work would never have come into being. We performed hundreds of hours of muscle testing—literally tens of thousands of tests—with our clients. We would come up with an idea and order the homeopathic vials to assess it from a vial maker on the West Coast. He must have thought we had a few screws loose because we ordered vials for auric fields, *chakras*, sounds, notes, octaves, letters of the alphabet. But we paid him and he sent us the vials. Then we would test enough clients to determine whether our ideas had any validity.

One of our most important early realizations about traditional energy clearings such as those used in NAET® and BioSET™ was that these techniques employ a typically "Western" focus on the physical—even though the techniques themselves use pure energy! In light of this internal contradiction—which was so obvious that at first, like trees in the forest, it was difficult to see—we became interested in the body's energy fields: specifically, the electromagnetic or auric fields.

The electromagnetic fields can be thought of as an interlocking set of high-frequency "force-fields," each responsible for the correct functioning of a particular gland, meridian, organ system, set of emotions, etc. Throughout this text I will focus attention on the electromagnetic fields. It should be remarked, however, that as the chakras (see Glossary) align with these fields in order and number, many of the same observations may also be applied to the chakras. The auric fields, combined with the system of chakras, form the human electromagnetic blueprint that can be envisioned as an energetic grid—a hologram—of intersecting horizontal and vertical lines of force (Figure 1).

Figure 1: The Human Bioenergy Blueprint
From the perspective of quantum biology, the human body is a hologram composed of intersecting lines of bioenergy. The above figure shows how the vertical, light-processing *chakras* interface with the horizontal, sound-generated electromagnetic fields to create the geometric matrix necessary for physical manifestation.

Many researchers have confirmed the existence of the human bioenergy fields. Kirlian photography has captured these fields for decades. In the 1980s Dr. Hiroshi Motoyama, a Japanese scientist, developed instrumentation capable of measuring bioluminescent electromagnetism such as light emitted from the chakras of yoga masters. Valerie Hunt, a professor at UCLA and author of *Infinite Mind: Science of the Human Vibrations of Consciousness*, has successfully employed an encephalograph (EEG) machine to register the auric fields. Dr. Hunt goes so far as to theorize that the mind, rather than residing in the brain, actually exists in the electromagnetic fields—and that in some as yet poorly understood way, the latter may *be* the mind.

In the main this is consistent with other scientific research indicating that the mind transcends the physical boundaries of the brain. Recent studies in immunological function conducted by Robert Jahn and Brenda Dunne, for example, concluded that mind or consciousness operates at the level of the immune system, which is directly responsible for distinguishing self from other. From a more esoteric perspective, gifted psychic and author Sheradon Bryce states point-blank: "Your mind is your electromagnetic field, your auric bands, or whatever you wish to call them. Your field is your mind. The thing in your head is your brain." Interestingly, anticipating our discussion of the "ener-genetic" similarities and distinctions between sound and light that begins in Chapter Six, Bryce often refers to the electromagnetic fields as "feeling *tones*" (my emphasis).

The Jewish alchemical science of the Kabala calls the auric fields collectively the *nefish,* often described as an iridescent bubble surrounding the body. In their book

Future Science, John White and Stanley Krippner point out that nearly a hundred different cultures refer to the human aura with nearly a hundred different names. The aura even appears as a halo around medieval images of Christian saints. One reason Western science has ignored the aura is that, because of its extremely high (actually higher-dimensional) frequency bands, it is hard to quantify. But it is worth noting that most scientists fail to understand the true nature of *any* energy field, not even one as mundane and measurable as electrical current.

As our electromagnetic blueprint, the auric fields function as a compendium of all the data pertinent to our wellbeing. In *The Holographic Universe* Michael Talbot explains, "Because an illness can appear in the energy field weeks and even months before it appears in the body, many ... believe that disease actually originates in the energy field. This suggests that the field is in some way more primary than the physical body." Naturopath Stephen Lindsteadt, author of *The Heart of Health: The Principles of Physical Health and Vitality,* explains that an "interruption or distortion in the range, strength and coherency of the body's electromagnetic system leads to breakdown in the body's self-healing mechanisms." Physician Richard Gerber, author of *Vibrational Medicine,* goes a step further by arguing that if doctors could find a way to treat the bioenergy field, they would achieve total healing. Until then, Dr. Gerber contends, many treatments "will not be permanent because we have not altered the basic [blueprint]."

Similarly, Nataliya Dobrova of the Galaxy Wave Group describes the individual as a "complex emotional bio-energy information system: a microcosm that reflects a macrocosm—the universe. All of a person's organs and systems have their own electromagnetic rhythms. Disharmony in this rhythmic activity signifies disease." Dr. Dobrova goes on to explain how such an "imbalance is closely connected with structural or functional problems found in a person's organs or systems. If one can restore the person's own rhythmic harmonies to a sick organ, one can restore the proper functions of that organ."[3]

The critical concept here is that all manifestations of disease, whether "physiological" or "psychological," result from disruption of the primary electromagnetic harmonies and rhythms contained in the auric fields and corresponding chakras. These bioenergy centers have an intimate relationship with DNA that gives them direct regulatory access to all cellular functions. If we can find a way to reset this bioenergy blueprint through harmonic resonance, we can go directly to the root of disease.

A nearly identical line of thinking informs one of the classics in the field of sound healing, Jonathan Goldman's *Healing Sounds: The Power of Harmonics.* Through harmonic resonance, writes Goldman, "it is possible to restore the natural vibratory frequencies of an object that may be out of tune or harmony. When an organ or another portion of the body is vibrating out of tune, we call this 'disease.'" Such belief in the power of harmonics to heal the body is echoed by Horowitz, whose research in cymatics (the study of the effects of sound on physical form) and electrogenetics leads him to emphasize that "harmonic frequencies maintain health, promote

---

[3] Quoted in Joe Champion, "Transdimensional Healing with the ADAM Technology."

growth and healing, while discordant frequencies produce stress, oxygen deprivation, acidification, electrochemical imbalances, illness and death."

From a cymatic or vibratory standpoint, *disharmony is disease*. The critical concept to grasp here is that all manifestations of disease, whether diagnosed as "physiological" or "psychological," result from disruption (in the form of toxicity or trauma) of the primary electromagnetic harmonies and rhythms contained in the auric fields and corresponding chakras. As I will elaborate in subsequent chapters, these bioenergy centers have an intimate relationship with DNA that gives them direct regulatory access to all cellular functions. Therefore, if we can find a way to reset our bioenergy blueprint through harmonic resonance, we can go directly to the root of disease processes. This was one of the principle goals Leigh and I set for ourselves as we began to develop the Regenetics Method.

4
Mapping the Bioenergy Fields

Having spent nearly eight years dying, I am deeply grateful for the pioneering work of Drs. Nambudripad and Cutler, without whom I do not know where (or even if) I would be today. Their inspiring techniques served as an indispensable springboard for the development of the Regenetics Method. But here I must point out two major blind spots with traditional energy clearings, at least as vehicles for resetting the body's electromagnetic blueprint.

The first oversight, to reiterate, is a predominant focus on physical issues without fully acknowledging their origins in our bioenergy fields. The second problem with traditional energy clearings is that the nervous system simply cannot process all the frequencies encoded like radio waves in our electromagnetic structure so as to transform a damaged blueprint. The same shortcoming applies to most—otherwise beneficial—energetic modalities, such as reiki and radionics, which function at the comparatively "surface" level of the nervous system as opposed to through DNA. Another way of stating this, one I trust will become clearer as we proceed, is that the majority of energetic therapies are "light-based," lacking the genetically transformational aspect of *sound* (Figure 8).

Contrary to the conservative paradigm that insists healing can only be achieved "one baby step at a time," my own experience and observation suggest that chronic illness in particular requires a *radical, simultaneous* bioenergy reset—one that can only be accomplished by way of DNA. "We wish to suggest a structure for the salt of deoxyribonucleic acid (DNA). This structure has novel features which are of considerable biological interest," announced James Watson and Francis Crick, DNA's discoverers, with an historical understatement in 1953. As this famous quote indicates, DNA is ironically named because it is technically a salt (sodium). Sodium is a critical human electrolyte and an excellent conductor of electromagnetism. Thus it is hardly surprising many researchers have determined that DNA directly regulates the body's electromagnetics.

Through extensive kinesiological research, Leigh and I identified more than 3,000 energy signatures over the body-mind-spirit continuum of the human electromagnetic blueprint. That is probably just the tip of the iceberg, but it has been enough to achieve often astonishing results. A traditional clearing of this size would far exceed the capacity of the healthiest nervous system. But when properly activated by sound combined with intention, *the superconductor that is DNA is designed to re-harmonize the entire bioenergy blueprint.*

When we speak of the body-mind-spirit continuum, we are not merely paying lip service to the interconnectedness of these elements. True healing means becoming "whole." Or as poet and metaphysical author Wynn Free eloquently puts it, healing is "that which removes ... the blockages from recognizing the existence of God within the self, and then becoming that Self."

Assisting someone to achieve wholeness (as opposed to mere symptom remission or, worse, suppression) cannot be accomplished without helping that person address the entire range of genetic, physical, mental, emotional, spiritual and karmic energies that are in disharmony.

We are touching on a critical distinction between curing, which usually involves the patient giving away his or her power to an outside source, and healing, which cannot be done for but only by a person. In order to establish and maintain total wellbeing, it behooves us to reconnect with our birthright of inherent health and vitality and understand that we ourselves are responsible for our healing.

We are touching on a critical distinction between *curing*, which usually involves the patient giving away his or her power to an outside source, typically a doctor trained in a limiting paradigm with respect to human potential, and *healing*, which in the final analysis cannot be done for but only *by* a person. In order to establish and maintain total wellbeing, it behooves us to reconnect with our birthright of inherent health and vitality and understand that we ourselves are responsible for our healing.

One of my mentors was an important figure in the field of radionics, a chiropractor named David Tansley. Dr. Tansley, along with Alice Bailey and Helena Blavatsky, provided some of the foundation for my notions about the electromagnetic fields. Following Tansley's lead, and supported by the quantum sciences' holographic view of the body, I began to understand the auric fields as our electromagnetic template, the blueprint for our physical form. My theory was that when "mapped," these fields would reveal themselves as "ecosystems" where a number of interdependent factors work either harmoniously to create vitality or disharmoniously to produce disease.

The approach Leigh and I took to map the electromagnetic fields was relatively straightforward. Using kinesiology with ourselves and our clients, we began muscle testing to establish which elements (genetic, physical, mental, emotional, etc.) were governed by which fields. We discovered an amazing poetic symmetry, a sacred geometry of almost breathtaking beauty in the way the fields are organized and work in concert.

This is the same sacred geometry that Horowitz references from an electrogenetic perspective and is intimately related to our molecular geometry that Merrill Garnett came to appreciate as music in his pioneering cancer research. "There is a harmony of the organism and a harmony in structure that allows the transfer of energy so that the organism can live and vibrate," writes Dr. Garnett. "Those harmonies and resonances recur and recreate the organism ... Ultimately, there is a musical or harmonic element within the organism ... This is molecular music, fragile, dependent, recurring under the right conditions, based in quantum echoes and hidden physics."

Sometimes, viewed from the perspective of disease, the musical and lyrical geometry of our bioenergy fields can appear very dark—recalling William Blake's "fearful symmetry"—but it is still poetry. For example, Leigh and I discovered that the third electromagnetic field is where cancer energies reside in many people. I emphasize "many people" because one of our other discoveries was that there are twelve different "Electromagnetic Groups."

Energetically, these twelve groups correspond to the twelve pairs of cranial nerves, with each group contributing to humanity's "collective Mind." These twelve groups also align with the twelve acupuncture meridians, the twelve months, the twelve signs of the zodiac, Earth's twelve tectonic plates, and even the biblical Twelve Tribes. What unites these very different energetic families is their shared "operating system": DNA.

Each Electromagnetic Group possesses a unique arrangement in its bioenergy blueprint that applies to all members.[4] This is truly an exciting revelation because in the context of DNA activation, it renders individual diagnosis unnecessary. Etymologically, *diagnosis* derives from Greek and means to "read through" in order to achieve knowledge or *gnosis*. But as it is too often practiced in today's medicine, diagnosis tends to oversimplify complex processes while "locking in" a disorder in the sufferer's mind until it seems that nothing, or very little, can be done. This mentality helps explain the emergence in recent years of such deflating phrases as "disease management."[5]

---

[4] See Appendix C for an example.

[5] "A numbing, unquestioned acceptance of a given medical prognosis can stem from a variety of foundational beliefs," writes Barbara Marciniak, "yet it will all boil down to a strong underlying belief in personal powerlessness ... The largely ineffective, costly health-care system is sustained by such beliefs." The need for someone else to be "in charge of fixing and taking care of the body has created a cumbersome bureaucracy to deal with cradle-to-grave health concerns that are, for the most part, founded on conditioned fears contrived in the mind."

By emphasizing the importance of the individual's commitment to conscious personal mastery as a prerequisite for becoming whole, the Regenetics Method represents a purposeful shift away from the diagnostic model.

The obsessive focus on labeling in the Western medical paradigm, combined with patients content to give away their power by consenting to being labeled, is arguably a main reason iatrogenic or doctor-induced deaths have become a crisis not only in the United States but in many parts of the world—with thousands of people dying unnecessarily under medical supervision every year. By emphasizing the importance of the individual's commitment to conscious personal mastery as a prerequisite for becoming whole, the Regenetics Method represents a purposeful shift away from the diagnostic model.

It is worth adding that Leigh and I also perform Regenetics sessions with nonattachment, intending only the client's highest good, since (as mentioned in Chapter One) studies have shown that non-directed prayer is statistically more effective in healing than prayer with an agenda. To "potentiate" a person, we simply use surrogate muscle-testing to determine the Electromagnetic Group, then apply the appropriate DNA activation.

But to return to the example of the third auric field. In addition to cancer energies, this field is also where we often find radiation energies. It is common knowledge there exists a direct link between cancer and radiation. Now, consider the emotional content of the third field. The primary emotions that exist in the energetic ecosystem with cancer and radiation are fear and related feelings of anxiety, worry, panic, and terror.

Now, guess which toxins show up in the third field. Chemicals. Pharmaceuticals. Drugs. Cigarettes. They are just sitting there in the third electromagnetic field contributing to cancer with radiation and fear. This cannot be coincidence. We live in a global culture that could be described as "Orwellian," take handfuls of toxic drugs for a headache, ingest aspartame on a daily basis, are continuously bombarded by radiation from computers, cellular telephones and microwave ovens, and have an alarmingly high incidence of cancer.

It took months and a lot of vials to map all the major energies in the body's electromagnetic fields. Leigh and I spent six months developing our ideas in South America, where we performed the first Potentiation Electromagnetic Repatterning on ourselves that restored my physical wellbeing and took care of Leigh's asthma and environmental allergies. Then we began offering Potentiation to others, many of whom have reported remarkable results as evidenced by the Testimonials provided in Appendix A.

In order to complete our work on Potentiation, however, we first had to set aside what we had been taught about DNA (that it is merely a biochemical protein-assembly code) and understand DNA's vitally reciprocal relationship with the body's electromagnetics. Only then were we in a position to explore avenues for stimulating the human genome's extraordinary self-healing potential.

5
Resetting the Bioenergy Blueprint via DNA

After mapping the electromagnetic fields, Leigh and I realized we had to find a way to press the "reset button" on this complex bioenergy blueprint. Coming from my NAET®/BioSET™ perspective, at first I thought we had to develop a technique to "clear" all the energies that were somehow "blocked." Going back to the example of the third electromagnetic field discussed in the previous chapter, I assumed that in order to begin addressing an entrenched condition like cancer, one somehow had to remove the energetic "roadblock" formed by radiation, fear-based emotions, pharmaceuticals, cigarettes, etc.

It was at this stage I began to understand that the nervous system was never meant to repattern the human bioenergy blueprint, that only DNA, our biocomputer, can build a new energy body, and that therefore, some other method of initiating electromagnetic repatterning besides acupressure stimulation of the meridian system had to be found.

We went to DNA because it was the obvious choice. DNA contains our genetic code and is the master blueprint for our biology. It literally creates us through a protein-assembly process known as transcription. In an article recently reprinted in *DNA Monthly*, Dr. Stephen Lindsteadt offers the following excellent summary of genetic transcription that takes into account both the biochemical and electromagnetic aspects of this life-creating process:

> The cell's innermost center is composed of ribonucleic acid and proteins (all molecules). The antenna or filament strand-like configuration of DNA allows the molecules to receive and transmit electromagnetic frequency information along its nucleotide bases, creating resonance reactions in genetic nucleotide triplets that create the template for the formation of messenger RNA (mRNA). Once mRNA has formed, it leaves the cell nucleus and attaches to structures known as ribosomes. Using raw material from cells, ribosomes produce proteins by following the sequence as instructed by mRNA. Proteins, in turn, go about their jobs inside or outside cells based on the original instructions passed down from the electromagnetic coding from DNA to RNA and finally to ribosomes. This process is known as *transcription* and provides the means for electromagnetic frequency oscillations, the body's master conductor, to interact with the cell's command center to instruct what notes to play, when, how loud, how long, etc., in order to maintain the precision and harmony of the whole body's vibratory and cellular orchestra.

To transcribe can be defined as to copy in writing, to produce in written form, or to arrange music for a different instrument. In other words, as the above quote suggests, we come into being, at our molecular level, through a process with striking affinities to *composition*.

It is extremely interesting to consider the privileged place of song, storytelling and words in creation myths. Anyone who has undertaken a comparative study of religions has probably been struck by the universal role of sound and language in such myths. Genesis 1:3 relates, "And God *said*, Let there be light: and there was light" (my emphasis). In the New Testament John states, "In the beginning was the Word," an idea paralleled in the *Vedas* where we read, "In the beginning was Brahman with whom was the Word."

The ancient Egyptians similarly believed that the god-men Thoth and Ra created life through language, just as the *Popul Vuh* from the Mayan tradition insists that the first humans were brought into existence by speech. Consistent with this language-based cosmology, the healing tradition immortalized in the Bock Saga originating in Finland is based on memorization and utterance of sacred sounds. This Saga, which Horowitz describes at length in *DNA: Pirates of the Sacred Spiral*, is an elaboration of a time-honored oral technology employing sound and light based on a "spiritual understanding of how to work with 'nature orally'"—or "naturally."

"Here, in ancient mythology," writes Horowitz, "is the relationship between genesis, genetics, and the spoken word. Also implied is the concept of wholistic health hinging on oral functions." Horowitz points out that today's neurophysiologists have determined that fully "one-third of the sensory-motor cortex of the brain is devoted to the tongue, oral cavity, the lips, and speech. In other words, oral frequency emissions (i.e., bioacoustic tones) spoken, or sung, exert powerful control over life, vibrating genes that influence total well-being and even evolution of the species."

Since the start of the Human Genome Project and the chromosomal mapping of the human genetic structure, there has been a tendency even in mainstream science to regard DNA as the alphabet through which we are, essentially, *written* into existence. Another metaphor often helpful in visualizing the somewhat complicated mechanism of genetic composition derives from music. The building of our protein structure, of our cells that form our tissues and organs, starts with RNA transcription of specific codes contained in DNA. We can imagine RNA as a magnetic recording tape that "plays" data stored in DNA as a composition of "notes" in the form of amino acids that create bars of "music" called proteins.

Leigh and I realized that if we were to activate what we saw as an extraordinary latent potential in DNA, one perhaps capable of transforming both consciousness and physiology we intuited along with a growing number of scientists including Lindsteadt, Horowitz, Gregg Braden and Bruce Lipton, we had to find or develop a way to access DNA without laboratories or test tubes. But how do you do that? How do you activate DNA without physically manipulating it?

At this stage we were fortunate enough to be given a copy of *The Cosmic Serpent: DNA and the Origins of Knowledge,* by French anthropologist Jeremy Narby. Dr. Narby spent years studying the healing techniques of shamans (medicine men) in the Amazon. His account, anthropologically as well as scientifically, is riveting and was particularly helpful in developing the Regenetics Method. In one telling passage, Narby writes, "DNA is not merely an informational molecule, but ... also a form of text and therefore ... is best understood by analytical ways of thinking commonly applied to other forms of text. For example, books."

Coming from my background in fiction writing and literary theory, this way of looking at DNA as a book was extremely appealing. More than anything, it just made sense. Narby is clearly saying we can learn to read DNA. By implication, he is suggesting we can also learn to write, or rewrite, the genetic code. This is how I can speak, in all seriousness, of "textual healing."

Narby is clearly saying we can learn to read DNA. By implication, he is suggesting we can also learn to write, or rewrite, the genetic code.

An alternative way to conceptualize what I am calling "rewriting" is to imagine that DNA contains a subtext resembling a series of footnotes that can be scrolled up onscreen. In this scenario, no rewriting or reprogramming is required. The program for our new and improved energy body already exists in what mainstream science has dismissed as "junk" DNA.

Most geneticists have admitted they have no idea why over ninety percent of our DNA even exists. This is especially provocative given that over ninety percent of our brain is also unused. Most of DNA appears to be nonsense. A lot of it is in the form of palindromes, puzzling sentences that read the same forward and backward. "Junk" DNA consists primarily of "introns," considered noncoding genetic sequences, as opposed to "exons" that have an identifiable coding function in building our protein structures through RNA transcription. In other words, as shown in Figure 2, exons clearly do something, while introns supposedly do not.

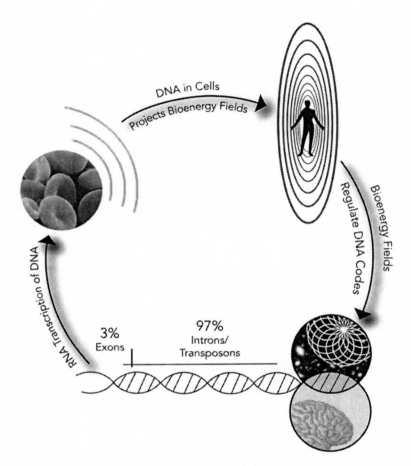

Figure 2: The Ener-genetic Composition Process
The above diagram illustrates how body building is both
genetic, involving RNA transcription of DNA codes to create
cells, and energetic, dependent on the interface between the
electromagnetic fields and "junk" or potential DNA for
regulation of cellular composition. This diagram also shows
how potential DNA's transposons can be directly prompted
by consciousness, internal (personal) and external
(universal), to modify cellular replication.

Fortunately, some who have asked how nature could be so inefficient are beginning to rethink this dogma that ultimately raises more questions than it answers. Recent research has shed light on intense "epigenetic" or alternative genetic activity in "junk" DNA, which appears to have much more to do with creating a specific species than previously thought. For example, if we only look at the small portion of DNA composed of exons, there is very little difference, genetically speaking, between a human being and a fruit fly! There is also practically nothing at the level of exons that distinguishes one human being from another.

Others who have studied the mystery of "junk" DNA have concluded the as little as three percent of the human genome directly responsible for protein transcription simply does not contain enough information to build *any* kind of body. Faced with this mystifying scenario, more and more scientists are paying attention to curious structures called "jumping DNA" or "transposons" found in the supposedly useless ninety-seven percent of the DNA molecule. In 1983 Barbara McClintock was awarded the Nobel prize for discovering transposons. She and fellow biologists coined the term *jumping DNA* for good reason, notes renowned psychic and scientific researcher David Wilcock, as "these one million different proteins can break loose from one area, move to another area, and thereby rewrite the DNA code."[6]

---

[6] Technically, transposons that jump to a new location using RNA are called "retrotransposons," of which there are three principle types—SINEs, LINEs, and HERVs—involved in large-scale genetic transformation. For the sake of simplicity, I will employ the term *transposon* to indicate all such structures capable of jumping from one chromosomal position to another.

Clearly, "junk" DNA was prematurely dismissed. In an article entitled "Genetics Beyond Genes" in the November 2003 issue of *Scientific American*, Dr. John Mattick, director of the Institute for Molecular Bioscience at the University of Brisbane, is quoted as saying that the failure to recognize the importance of introns (to say nothing of transposons) in "junk" DNA "may well go down as one of the biggest mistakes in the history of molecular biology." Leigh and I propose we rename "junk" DNA *potential DNA* and understand it as the human organism's ener-genetic interface with a higher-dimensional "life-wave" responsible for giving rise to a particular physical form through RNA transcription of DNA codes. We will return to this critically important idea a bit later.

Leigh and I propose we rename "junk" DNA potential DNA and understand it as the human organism's ener-genetic interface with a higher-dimensional "life-wave" responsible for giving rise to a particular physical form through RNA transcription of DNA codes.

DNA, whether coding or noncoding, whether exons, introns or transposons, is composed of an "alphabet" of four basic "letters" called nucleotides that combine to form sixty-four different "words" used to build a virtually limitless number of "sentences" called genes. The number 64 is especially interesting given another of our inspirations, J. J. Hurtak's *The Keys of Enoch. The Keys of Enoch* is an elaboration of the "keys" for creating a higher energy body. Significantly, there are sixty-four keys, just as there are sixty-four nucleotide combinations.

Hurtak is clearly writing about actualizing a transformational potential in our genetics.

I realize this is a lot of information, especially for the lay reader, for whom I have endeavored to simplify this material as much as possible. As these concepts are among some of the most life-changing I have personally encountered in my research, I encourage you to go over this chapter and any others that seem complicated as many times as necessary until the ideas sink in. To summarize to this point, it is accurate to say that DNA is a form of text with its own alphabet, and that we can learn to read as well as rewrite DNA, in the process activating the genetic program designed to turn our introns into exons (via transposons) and create new protein transcription sequences that lead to regeneration, or *re-gene-ration.*

6
Sound, Intention & Genetic Healing

In a very intriguing section of *The Cosmic Serpent,* Narby includes snippets from his personal journals. One entry is of particular interest at this point in our discussion of DNA:

> According to shamans of the entire world, one established communication with spirits via music. For [shamans] it is almost inconceivable to enter the world of spirits and remain silent. Angelica Gebhart Sayer discusses the visual music projected by the spirits in front of the shaman's eyes. It is made up of three-dimensional images that coalesce into sound, and that the shaman imitates by emitting corresponding melodies.

In a provocative footnote to himself, Narby adds, "I should check whether DNA emits sound or not."

One school of thought insists that humans are actually made of sound and that DNA itself may be a form of sound. Drawing on meticulously documented research, Horowitz explains that DNA emits and receives both phonons and photons, or electromagnetic waves of sound and light. In the 1990s, according to Horowitz, "three Nobel laureates in medicine advanced research that revealed the primary function of DNA lies not in protein synthesis ... but in electromagnetic energy reception and transmission. Less than three percent of DNA's function involves protein manufacture; more than ninety percent functions in the realm of bioacoustic and bioelectric signaling." In recent years a fascinating artistic field called DNA music has even begun to flourish. It therefore seems appropriate, at the very least, to compare DNA to a keyboard with a number of keys that produce the music of life.

But what if on some level we *are* made of sound? What if in the beginning *was* the Word? What if the music of the spheres is no myth? What if we ourselves are a harmonic convergence? What if the holographic grid of our being is a linguistic and musical interface between higher-dimensional light, which might be considered a form of divine thought or *intention*, and *sound* in higher-dimensional octaves? After all, String theory, which has become popular lately in the scientific community, posits the existence of many different, theoretically accessible dimensions that appear notationally linked much like strings on a guitar.

Narby repeatedly makes the point that shamans use sound because this allows them to transform some aspect of the genetic code. If DNA is indeed a text, a keyboard, a musical score; if it is true this score can be rewritten so that it plays a new type of music; and if we live not just in a holographic but in a *harmonic* universe, then it seems entirely plausible, returning to an earlier idea, that our electromagnetic fields are concentric spheres of multidimensional sound.

When Leigh and I began developing the Regenetics Method, we discovered through muscle testing that each of the nine electromagnetic fields corresponds not just to a chakra but to one of nine third-dimensional sound octaves. Energetically, our research indicates that at our present evolutionary stage, humans are built of a vertical series of nine light-processing chakras interfacing with nine concentric auric fields (which are sonic in nature) to form the three-dimensional holographic matrix that produces our physical body. Through DNA activation, as detailed in the next chapter, this bioenergy blueprint can be upgraded to an "infinity circuit" based on eight chakras and eight fields (Figures 1 and 3).

Moreover, it appears from ongoing research that at the genetic level, sound gives rise to light—a microcosmic assertion consistent with the basic macrocosmology underwriting the Regenetics Method elaborated in subsequent chapters. In a paper entitled "A Holographic Concept of Reality" appearing in *Psychoenergetic Systems* as far back as 1975, a team of researchers headlined by Richard Alan Miller first outlined a compelling model of ener-genetic composition resulting in "precipitated reality": "Superposed coherent waves of different types in the cells interact to form diffraction patterns, firstly in the acoustic [sound] domain, secondly in the electromagnetic [light] domain." This leads to the manifestation of physical form as a "quantum hologram—a translation between acoustical and optical holograms." Significantly, this sound-light translation mechanism that creates the somatic experience of reality functions in the genome.

This is not the place to provide a full treatment of the impressive science of quantum bioholography. Rather, I wish to emphasize that according to this model that is attracting many proponents as more and more of its precepts are confirmed, it is becoming apparent that DNA directs cellular metabolism and replication not just biochemically but electromagnetically through a chromosomal mechanism that translates sound into light waves, and vice versa. According to the holographic model of genetic expression, sound and light, or phonons and photons, establish a sophisticated communication network throughout the physical organism that extends into the bioenergy fields and back to the cellular and subcellular levels (Figure 2).

Recalling Edgar Cayce's prediction that "sound would be the medicine of the future," Jonathan Goldman in *Healing Sounds: The Power of Harmonics* coined the following inspirational formula: sound + intention = healing. If we define intention as a form of conscious light energy equivalent to thought, an idea consistent with many shamanic traditions such as that of the Toltecs of Mesoamerica, we can translate Goldman's formula as:

SOUND + LIGHT = HEALING.

Recently, the ability of sound and light to heal DNA was scientifically documented by a Russian research team of geneticists and linguists. Russian linguists discovered that the genetic code, especially that in potential DNA, follows uniform grammar and usage rules virtually identical to those of human languages. This invalidates many modern linguistic theories by proving that language did not appear randomly but reflects humanity's shared genetics. In *The God Code* Gregg Braden further demonstrates that the ancient four-letter Hebrew name for God (YHVH, the Tetragrammaton) is actually code for DNA based on the latter's chemical composition of nitrogen, oxygen, hydrogen, and carbon. This assertion, with its vast implications relative to DNA's universal role as a divine language spoken through the body, has been peer-reviewed and accepted by many scholars of Hebrew.

Fritz Albert Popp's Nobel prize-winning research establishes that every cell in the body receives, stores and emits coherent light in the form of biophotons. In tandem with biophonons, biophotons maintain electromagnetic frequency patterns in all living organisms. In the words of Stephen Lindsteadt, this matrix that is produced and sustained by frequency oscillations "provides the energetic switchboarding behind every cellular function, including DNA/RNA messengering. Cell membranes scan and convert signals into electromagnetic events as proteins in the cell's bi-layer change shape to vibrations of specific resonant frequencies." Emphasizing that every "biochemical reaction is preceded by an electromagnetic signal," Lindsteadt concludes, "Cells communicate both electromagnetically and chemically and create biochemical pathways that interconnect all functions of the body."

Russian biophysicists Peter Gariaev and Vladimir Poponin have also explored DNA's extraordinary electromagnetic properties. Their research reveals that DNA has a special ability to attract photons, causing the latter to spiral along the helix-shaped DNA molecule instead of proceeding along a linear path. In other words, DNA has the amazing ability—unlike any other molecule known to exist—to bend or weave light around itself.

In addition, it appears that a previously undetected form of intelligent light or intention energy (emanating from higher dimensions and distinguishable from both gravity and electromagnetic radiation) which Dr. Eli Cartan first termed "torsion" in 1913 after its twisting movement through the fabric of space-time, gives rise to DNA. Many decades later, the concept of torsion energy was still alive and well enough to inspire an entire generation of Russian scientists, who authored thousands of papers on the subject in the 1990s alone. "A unified subliminal field of potentially universal consciousness apparently exists," writes Horowitz on the subject of the Russian studies, "and may be explained as emerging from a previously overlooked physical vacuum or energy matrix."

The ancient Greeks were well aware of this potent energy, calling it "aether" and understanding that it is directly responsible for universal manifestation. In the 1950s Russian scientist Nicolai Kozyrev conclusively proved the existence of this life-giving subspace energy, demonstrating that, like time, it flows in a sacred geometric spiral resembling the involutions of a conch shell that has been called phi, the Golden Mean, and the Fibonacci sequence. In the face of overwhelming evidence of its existence, Western scientists are returning to the notion of aether using such phrases as "zero point energy" and "vacuum potential."[7] Recently, physicists Richard

---

[7] At the time of this writing, a new model called the Electric Universe theory is beginning to challenge the notion of zero point energy and the like by suggesting that such "missing matter," rather than being "multidimensional," actually exists in an electrical, or plasma, state in our own dimension. If true, the Electric Universe theory could potentially do away with the Big Bang by demonstrating that the universe is continuously self-generating and thus has no beginning. The relationship between matter in an electrified plasma state and torsion energy has yet to be coherently described. Theoretically as well

Feynman and John Wheeler went so far as to calculate that the amount of torsion energy contained in a light bulb could literally bring the world's oceans to a boil!

This breakthrough research in the temporal physics of subspace establishes that torsion energy permeates the entire multidimensional galaxy and not only is responsive to but may actually *be* consciousness creatively experiencing itself in time. "To put it as bluntly as possible," writes David Wilcock, "you cannot separate consciousness and torsion waves—they are the same thing. When we use our minds to think, we are creating movements of electrical impulses in the brain, and when any electrical energy moves, torsion waves are also created."

This breakthrough research in the temporal physics of subspace establishes that torsion energy permeates the entire multidimensional galaxy and not only is responsive to but may actually be consciousness creatively experiencing itself in time.

According to the Russian findings, notes Wynn Free, "this spiraling 'torsion' energy could actually be the substance of our human souls, and is therefore the precursor to the DNA molecule ... It already exists in the fabric of space and time before any physical life emerges." Elsewhere, Free remarks of transposons that these tiny segments of DNA can travel along the genome activating different parts of it when prompted by consciousness. In keeping with Dr. Gariaev's "Wave-based Genome" theory, Free concludes that DNA functions "somewhat like a

---

as practically, the two could be intimately related. See Footnote 20 in Chapter Fourteen.

computer chip, with different sections that can either be 'on' or 'off.'" Thus we can easily imagine how the torsion waves of human consciousness could program, or reprogram, DNA's binary code (Figure 2).

Similarly, the Gariaev group demonstrated that chromosomes function much like (re)programmable holographic biocomputers employing DNA's own electromagnetic radiation. Their research strongly suggests that human DNA is literally composed of genetic "texts"; that chromosomes both produce and receive the information contained in these texts in order to encode and decode them, respectively; and that chromosomes assemble themselves into a holographic grating or lattice designed to generate and interpret highly stable spiral standing waves (frequency oscillations) of sound and light that direct all biological functions. In other words, explain longtime genetics researchers Iona Miller and Richard Miller in an article reprinted in *DNA Monthly* based partly on Gariaev's findings entitled "From Helix to Hologram," the genetic "code is transformed into physical matter, guided by light and sound signals."

Decades of research by Japanese scientist Kikuo Chishima substantiate this assertion. Dr. Chishima's work strongly suggests that red blood cells are formed not in bone marrow, as is commonly believed, but in the intestinal villi. Red blood cells appear to be 1) guided by systemic frequency oscillations in the bioenergy blueprint and 2) capable of synthesizing DNA in order to differentiate into specific types of cells, which then migrate via the 90,000-mile-long capillary system to wherever they are needed. Writes Lindsteadt, "This open-ended system that connects to the lymphatic system, the meridian system and the connective tissue provides communication pathways for the flow of information and cellular instructions from the electromagnetic energy matrix."

One revolutionary implication (of many) of this research is that, to activate DNA and stimulate healing on the cellular level, one can simply use our species' supreme expression of creative consciousness: words.

One revolutionary corollary (of many) of this research is that, to activate DNA and stimulate healing on the cellular level, one can simply use our species' supreme expression of creative consciousness: words. While Western researchers clumsily cut and splice genes, Gariaev's team developed sophisticated devices capable of influencing cellular metabolism through sound and light waves keyed to human language frequencies. Using this method, Gariaev proved that chromosomes damaged by X-rays, for instance, can be repaired. Moreover, this was accomplished *noninvasively* by simply applying vibration and language, or sound combined with intention, or *words*, to DNA.

According to Iona Miller and Richard Miller, "Life is fundamentally electromagnetic rather than chemical, the DNA blueprint functioning as a biohologram which serves as a guiding matrix for organizing physical form." Arguably the most far-reaching implication of the research cited in this chapter is that DNA can be activated through conscious linguistic expression (somewhat like an antenna) to reset the bioenergy fields, which in turn (like orbiting communication satellites) can transmit radio and light signals to restore proper cellular structure and functioning of the human body.

7
Sealing the Fragmentary Body

Those with highly evolved consciousness such as spiritual teachers have always insisted that the human body is genetically (re)programmable by words in the form of songs, poems, prayers, affirmations, or mantras. The words must be harmonically attuned to the organism and the intention behind them impeccable. This is why although DNA activation has become trendy, results can vary enormously. The more advanced the individual healer's consciousness, the less need there is for machines. Gariaev himself suggests one can achieve comparable results unassisted. It is my personal belief that the individual can achieve far superior results than is possible with machines.

Citing a variety of scientific studies that prove sound can change human brainwaves as well as heartbeat and respiration, Goldman highlights the developments in the field of sound therapy credited to such medical pioneers as Dr. John Diamond, Dr. Peter Manners and Barbara Hero, all of whom have designed mechanical instruments for healing through sound. Clearly, however, Goldman believes that human voice is the ultimate healing instrument. Some shamanic healers insist that the transformative power of human voice cannot be digitally reproduced and retain its full character—that the digital recording is comparable to a clone, "possessing form but lacking spirit"—which leads me to question the effectiveness of DNA activation CDs and similar technologies.

Allow me to direct your attention to the notion, found in so many religions and mythologies, of a "fall from grace" that created a rift in the universe, a disruptive force that engendered duality and the experience of separation. In Christianity this is often termed "original sin." In one Hindu myth, human consciousness began as a tiny ripple that chose to leave the ocean of cosmic consciousness. As it awoke to itself, our consciousness forgot it was part of the infinite cosmic ocean and found itself washed ashore and imprisoned in a state of isolation. Wilcock calls this perceived separation from Source the "Original Wound" and remarks that it is "the basis behind all suffering, and also ... the final key to enlightenment."

Science has its own versions of the fundamental duality at the heart of existence. The particle-wave duality, in which atomic components are simultaneously particles and waves, is a primary example. Not surprisingly, DNA has also been shown to possess a version of the particle-wave binarism. "In accordance with this duality," writes Horowitz, "DNA codes all living organisms in two ways, both with the assistance of DNA matter involving RNA and enzymes for protein synthesis, and by DNA sign wave functions, including coding at its own laser radiation level that functions bioholographically" (Figure 2).

From the outset the holographic model has focused on the duality inherent in human experience. Dr. Karl Pribram first theorized a neural hologram in the brain's cerebral cortex operating in tandem with a subatomic or universal hologram—a micro-macrocosmic fractal interface summed up by Horowitz when he states that "a hologram within a hologram produces life as a function of creative consciousness." In *Wholeness and the Implicate Order*, Dr. David Bohm also describes the brain as a hologram designed to interpret a larger hologram—the cosmos. "In this dualistic holographic model," explains Horowitz, "inseparable interconnectedness of holographs, including that of the Creator with the created, underlies human existence." Human existence, in turn, to quote Iona Miller and Richard Miller, is rooted in genes serving as "holographic memories of the existential blueprint."

As mentioned earlier, through kinesiological testing Leigh and I discovered and mapped a total of nine electromagnetic fields in humans. I offer that the initial blueprint for our creation, however, was one in which instead of nine, we had only eight fields corresponding to eight chakras. This is a pivotal concept for anyone interested in genuine, permanent healing. There are many reasons why I insist that our true bioenergy blueprint is based on the number 8. The one I offer now is of a visual nature. What do you get when you turn the number 8 on its side? An infinity sign. This is our infinite nature, our divine birthright expressed in a symbol.

Perhaps you are familiar with the theosophical teachings of Bailey and Blavatsky or Tansley's writings on radionics. All three present a model of the human bioenergy template with only seven fields. Vedic teachings are also based on seven energy centers. But kinesiologically, at this stage of human development there are clearly nine fields, not counting a tenth we call the Source or Master Field that corresponds in astrophysical terms to Galactic Center (as covered in detail in Part II) and to *Nezah* or Eternity in the kabalistic Tree of Life.

Figures 3a & 3b: Sealing the Fragmentary Body
The first image (Figure 3a) shows a typical human bioenergy blueprint with nine electromagnetic fields/*chakras* and a Fragmentary Body, envisioned as an energetic disruption in the second field/chakra from the bottom. The second image (Figure 3b) shows a "potentiated" bioenergy blueprint with an "infinity circuit" of eight fields/chakras. Note how sealing the Fragmentary Body replaces fragmentation and duality with harmony and sacred geometry, allowing for the free flow of bioenergy throughout the body.

Figure 3b.

Bailey, Blavatsky and Tansley were right, however, when it comes to the second electromagnetic field. This field (with the corresponding "sex" chakra) has been called the *Fragmentary Body* (Figure 3a). When mentioned in the esoteric literature, the Fragmentary Body is considered highly problematic. This is because the second electromagnetic field resonates as a "Frankenstein's monster" of energies that simply do not add up, that in many cases do not even appear to belong in the human body. For example, energies associated with all types of parasites attach to the second field.

In every other electromagnetic field that governs a population of microorganisms, many of these are beneficial and undoubtedly belong in the body. For instance, in the seventh field of the Electromagnetic Group whose structure is shown in Appendix C, we find intestinal flora, which play a crucial role in creating a healthy biological terrain. But in the second field we find only parasites, which—far from contributing to health—siphon off the host's life energy.

Each electromagnetic field also governs specific organ systems. The two organ systems found in the second field of all Electromagnetic Groups are the reproductive system and the mouth: our (pro)creative systems. The intimate relationship between these seemingly distinct systems appears in the way we conceptualize and describe creativity. Authors "give birth" to a novel, "conceive" an idea, just as a poetic organ called the uterus "utters" a fetus into the world.

Developing the Regenetics Method led Leigh and myself overwhelmingly to a cosmology with a creation scenario where something disruptive occurred. This is not a judgment, simply an observation. In the beginning was literally the Word, and something divisive resulted. Somebody spoke and birthed a dualistic universe of opposites and separation, one with a Great Rift running through the middle mirrored overhead in the Milky Way.[8] In the microcosm of our energy body, in keeping with the ancient dictum "As above, so below," this Great Rift or Original Wound manifests as the second electromagnetic field.

We can envision the Fragmentary Body as an energetic vacuum that to a large degree separates spirit and matter by keeping higher-dimensional torsion energy from filling our electrogenetic matrix until we become "enlightened" in the flesh.

We can envision the Fragmentary Body as an energetic vacuum that to a large degree separates spirit and matter by keeping higher-dimensional torsion energy from filling our electrogenetic matrix until we become "enlightened" in the flesh. The word *enlighten* literally means to light up, to illuminate. The Fragmentary Body is an anti-enlightenment consciousness vacuum, a systemic bioenergy drain that, until "sealed," limits our ability to embody the light of higher consciousness. When properly sealed through DNA activation, however, this field that once represented an energetic liability becomes the locus for the human being's healing into a consciousness and physiology capable of expressing divine radiance.

---

[8] On this subject Judith Bluestone Polich writes, "The 2012 alignment occurs when the December solstice sun conjuncts the crossing point of the Milky Way in Sagittarius. An area in the sky called the dark rift—known to the Maya as the Xibalba bi, the road to the underworld—points right to this crossing point. The crossing point is found at the center of our galaxy, and the Maya called it the sacred tree. To them it indicated the place of creation." See Part II.

* * *

Physicists have recently begun to acknowledge the existence of particles called tachyons, a powerful form of energy popularized by *Star Trek*. But tachyons are not science fiction. Tachyons are particle-waves belonging to the lepton family that, according to the evidence, fail to obey the law of gravity. In other words, they appear to travel faster than light.

Even normal quantum particles such as electrons have been shown to communicate "telepathically" with each other at a distance, as if indeed connected at an aetheric level. As previously remarked, some members of the scientific community have gone so far as to resurrect the Greek term *aether* for the torsion-wave medium that is "empty" space. A variety of other scientific phrases, including "dark energy" and "quantum medium," have been employed in recent years to indicate the astounding energetic potential of what has for the past century been incorrectly perceived as nothingness.

Similar findings have been reached in biology. Molecular scientists have identified a striking phenomenon mentioned in the previous chapter—zero point energy—by which biological organisms use measurably more energy than is possible for them to extract from their daily intake of food, water, and air. This phenomenon occurs when the distance between two non-charged surfaces, such as water and a cell membrane, becomes negligible, dimensional coherence ("lasing") occurs and, by most indications, multidimensional torsion energy is drawn from the vacuum potential of the space matrix.

For those familiar with the officially acknowledged applications of Einstein's theories of Relativity, it should be easy to see how the mere existence of particles that move faster than light and/or communicate telepathically through an aetheric medium begins to unravel an entire paradigm for understanding the physical universe.[9] On the subject of the "Crumbling of Certainty" in the wake of such logic-challenging discoveries in quantum physics, Charles Eisenstein writes, "The whole idea of certainty of knowledge, built through objective reasoning, is only as sound as the objectivity at its basis. Question that, and we question the soundness of the entire edifice of experimentally-derived knowledge" on which our current sciences, and the worldview connected to them, depend.

Thus we find ourselves in the age of "subquantum" science, in which our greatest minds find themselves struggling to explain seemingly inexplicable phenomena having to do with apparently impossible, nonlocal events such as remote viewing and ESP—to cite two puzzling examples that can now be plausibly explained as intelligent movements of higher-dimensional torsion energy or universal creative consciousness. I propose that tachyons and related particle-waves are forms of non-gravitationally-bound or superluminal torsion energy emanating multidimensionally from our point of origin at the center of our galaxy.

The Vedics created an elaborate science spanning yoga, meditation and diet for pooling this higher-dimensional energy, which they termed "prana," into their

---

[9] Although it is generally assumed in Western scientific circles that Einstein's theories automatically do away with the need for a unified energy field, in the 1920s Einstein actually affirmed the contrary, stating that "in theoretical physics, we cannot get along without" such a field—which, interestingly, he referred to as "ether."

bodies. The Taoists developed a similar science for cultivating "chi." Early in the 20th Century, Nikola Tesla theorized the existence of "scalar" waves (subsequently popularized by Tom Bearden) that transcend spatial limitations and are capable of acting instantaneously at a distance. Tesla created a prototype scalar system for free electricity using no generators or wires. Later, Wilhelm Reich became famous experimenting with "orgone" energy. Aether, *prana, chi,* scalar, orgone—all are names for the light-based aspect of the same spiritual or torsion energy that gave (and continues to give) rise to the holographic multiverse.

My research suggests that life as we know it depends on a double helix, structurally similar to DNA, of two differentiated, interfacing types of torsion energy: 1) higher-dimensional thought or *intention* manifesting as light; and 2) *sound* in higher-dimensional octaves which, like its counterpart, is measurable as a standing spiral wave capable of activating DNA, for example, with no time lapse across theoretically infinite distances.

The DNA molecule is brilliantly designed as a holographic torsion-wave-decoding biocomputer— one that magnetizes creative energy to it, and thus to our consciousness, that is aligned with our beliefs.

To those wondering how such waves could contain sufficient information to (re)program DNA, it is worth remembering we live in a world crisscrossed with electromagnetic waves that carry highly complex television, telephone and radio signals that can be easily decoded with the right equipment. According to Richard Miller, a leading theoretician in the field of quantum bioholography, even more information can be holographically encoded than with simple electromagnetic encryption. For practical purposes, the DNA molecule is brilliantly designed as a holographic torsion-wave-decoding biocomputer—one that magnetizes creative energy to it, and thus to our consciousness, that is aligned with our beliefs.

What if, by introducing healing sounds and intentions to the genome, sounds and intentions that derive from the same unified torsion energy of Source that I will argue in Part II is unconditional love, it is possible to key transposons in potential DNA to rearrange themselves and play the energy body in a higher octave, one more in tune with the unlimited creative consciousness of nonlocalized mind? What if we can thus raise the harmonics of our system of electromagnetic fields and fully align ourselves with our Higher Selves? What if by raising our vibratory frequency from within, we can repattern our electromagnetic blueprint and seal the Fragmentary Body, allowing us to transcend limiting dualistic patterns and elements related to these patterns—physical, mental, emotional, and spiritual?

Again referencing the new Russian research in "wave-genetics," Wilcock writes that "these studies give extremely convincing evidence that the DNA molecule is directly affected by outside energy sources. If DNA is actually assembled by an outside source of energy, then when we increase the flow of that energy into the DNA, we can also expect that the health and vitality of the organism will increase." Wilcock concludes that we "are left with the strong impression that torsion waves are the single most important factor in an organism's health."

Leigh and I think of ourselves not as "practitioners" or "healers" but merely as facilitators for the individual's own bioenergetic unfoldment. We consider Potentiation Electromagnetic Repatterning the first step in a three-part "rebirth cycle" that continues with Articulation Bioenergy Enhancement and culminates in Elucidation Triune Activation. This process starts with a specific DNA activation that initiates a domino effect of electromagnetic repatterning that, like human gestation, takes just over nine months (42 weeks) to unfold.

Because there are two forms of higher-dimensional helical waves that interface with potential DNA, sound and light, Potentiation employs both. We use sound (produced vocally) and light (in the form of a non-directed healing intention) to produce what we call an "energized narrative." We contend that this conscious movement of torsion energy in the form of special words is capable of stimulating transposons in the human genome, activating a reset program that lies dormant in potential DNA. This program (which we do not need to create because it already exists) starts a chain reaction in which torsion energy works its way down and up then down again through the various subtle bodies on a gestational timeline.

Sealing is an indispensable step on the path to true healing, as it lays the groundwork for a higher energy body—and ultimately enlightenment—by initiating the process of integrating the fragmentation of the Self caused by duality.

After five months, the electromagnetic fields and chakras recalibrate from nine to eight in number and the bioenergy vacuum constituted by the second field/chakra, the Fragmentary Body, seals itself. This occurs as the ninth and second fields/chakras fuse in what might be

Figure 4: Energizing the Bioenergy Blueprint
The above image shows the flow of torsion energy or universal creative consciousness down through the electromagnetic fields that occurs during Potentiation. Utilizing the genetic sound-light translation mechanism, each sonic field, in turn, energizes the corresponding *chakra* with higher-dimensional light, which then transfers as bioenergy or *kundalini* to specific aspects of the subtle anatomy.

termed a sacred marriage of opposites. Sealing, I cannot overemphasize, is an indispensable step on the path to true healing, as it lays the groundwork for a higher energy body—and ultimately enlightenment—by initiating the process of integrating the fragmentation of the Self caused by duality (the Original Wound). In a profound sense, we can say that *sealing is required for healing or "wholing."*

Over the next four months, this new bioenergy blueprint begins to fill with Source energy from the top down much like a tiered fountain as shown in Figure 4. The chakras slowly begin to open, becoming more powerful and efficient, as the electromagnetic fields gradually increase their harmonic resonance. At this point, "potentiators" often report a sense of integrating this new energy that can last up to an additional gestational cycle of nine months.

In terms of consciousness, Potentiation Electromagnetic Repatterning facilitates awareness of the true nature of the Self (which is divine) and the Cosmos (which is holographic, meaning the part not only reflects but contains the whole), empowering individual discernment to begin attracting higher "quantum outcomes" following the universal law that "consciousness creates."[10] This productive use of awareness invites one to begin facing limiting thoughts, emotions and beliefs and by itself can lead to markedly increased vitality, more balanced interactions with one's environment (i.e., fewer allergic reactions), greater financial abundance, more loving relationships, even renewed life purpose.

---

[10] See Part II.

70

Articulation Bioenergy Enhancement is appropriate as of the five-month mark of Potentiation, after the electromagnetic fields have recalibrated and sealing has occurred. At this point a new bioenergy blueprint (with no interruption or leakage in the form of the Fragmentary Body) is in place to utilize the potent life force Articulation stimulates. In Vedic teachings this life force is called *kundalini*. Leigh and I understand kundalini as the individual's own torsion life-wave that, again following "As above, so below," marries the macro- with the microcosmic in the process of healing. Articulation gently "switches on" kundalini first at the genetic and cellular levels, providing a continuous bioenergy supply for creativity and personal transformation in all areas—including artistic expression, interpersonal communication, healthy sexuality, and rebuilding through diet and exercise.

Elucidation Triune Activation, the third and final phase of the Regenetics Method, is appropriate following Articulation as of the nine-month (42-week) mark of Potentiation. Elucidation stimulates a mostly dormant portion of the neocortex or triune brain, facilitating creation of a higher energy body. Elucidation also encourages transcendence by assisting the individual to replace limiting and/or harmful beliefs with life-affirming ones. This restructuring of the belief system, the most fundamental creational level of human subtle anatomy, can dramatically change one's experience of reality. The ultimate goal is the embodiment of a new awareness based no longer on duality and separation but on unity consciousness and unconditional love.

8
A Practical Application of Era III Medicine

By way of closing this section, I wish to return briefly to the work of Larry Dossey and address one practical application of Era III medicine. Dr. Dossey writes, "Recently modern scientists have discovered that nonlocal events, meaning events that don't happen where they're initiated necessarily, are not fantasy but are part of the fabric of the universe." Citing well-known physicist Nick Herbert, Dossey enumerates three primary characteristics of nonlocal events. Nonlocal events, he says, are:

1) *unmediated*, meaning you do not necessarily need a transmission field for a nonlocal event to occur, that it occurs even in the absence of an identifiable field;
2) *unmitigated*, meaning their strength does not fall off through time or distance; and
3) *immediate,* sometimes even anachronistic, meaning they can happen before they happen.

On many occasions, Leigh and I have found that our clients have begun to feel Potentiation Electromagnetic Repatterning happening before the actual session. Time and space seem irrelevant with the Regenetics Method, which is what one would expect working with torsion energy capable of moving faster than observable light.

Here again, Gariaev's research provides a plausible explanation. The Russian team found that DNA can cause "disturbance patterns" in space, generating small electromagnetic wormholes of a subquantum nature. These microscopic DNA-activated wormholes, similar in their ability to bend light to the nonlocal energy signatures found in the vicinity of black holes, including Galactic Center, are connections between different areas in the multiverse through which data (such as sound and light codes designed to assist human evolution) can be transmitted outside the space-time continuum. *Remote healing, for example, is thus reasonably explained as an ener-genetic phenomenon.*

Finally, after much research, Leigh and I formulated our ideas and performed the first Potentiation on ourselves while still living in South America. Initially, to be perfectly honest, I did not experience any significant shifts. But after a few weeks, I realized I was beginning to crave foods I had been unable to eat for years. Starches mostly, carbohydrates.

Leigh theorized I was craving starches again because my body was starting to cleanse and was asking for foods to help bind toxicity from my cells and escort it out of my system without further damaging my tissues. She suggested that I try some of the foods I had been craving such as pasta, bread, rice, and potatoes. So I began eating them, timidly at first but with increasing gusto as it became obvious they were no longer overrunning me with Candida or causing unbearable bloating.

If Potentiation had stopped there, we both knew we had been given an extraordinary gift. Nothing else had been able to restore my ability to enjoy the full range of foods. But Potentiation did not stop there. I began getting back greater and greater levels of vitality and was able to start exercising again. Within six months, I returned to swimming a mile without stopping. I had been unable to perform anywhere close to this for nearly seven years. Two and a half years later, I can swim two miles at full speed, which is more than I could do in my twenties before the onset of my illness.

I began getting back greater and greater levels of vitality and was able to start exercising again. Within six months, I returned to swimming a mile without stopping. I had been unable to perform anywhere close to this for nearly seven years.

My body was recovering its inherent wisdom that had been undermined by vaccines and was beginning to harmonize with the natural environment again. The experience reminded me of a story from Greek mythology about a giant named Antaeus who wrestles Hercules. Antaeus derived his great strength from his connection with Earth. Every time Hercules tried to pin him, Antaeus would simply touch the ground and grow exponentially stronger. Finally, when he was almost spent, Hercules realized the only way to defeat Antaeus was to lift him off the ground where he could no longer draw strength from Earth. This was how Hercules strangled and killed Antaeus.

A month after Potentiation, for the first time in nearly eight years, I felt as if Hercules had finally set me back on the ground. I knew intuitively, as well as experientially, that I was again drawing strength from food, water, and sunlight. Something altogether profound was happening in me. Leigh also underwent an ener-genetic transformation with many tangible results that, to our amazement, included the partial straightening of her lifelong scoliosis that not even a back brace, regular chiropractic treatments and intensive Rolfing® had been able to modify.

We wanted to share Potentiation with family and friends, but were still living on another continent. One of my mentors suggested we could do this work at a distance using the elements we were already using: sound and intention. This struck me as very much in line with Dossey's notions of Era III medicine and nonlocalized mind.

We began to explore the possibility of performing Potentiation at a distance. One technique we looked to for ideas was radionics. Radionics is a type of energy medicine that has historically been performed remotely. There is some very substantial proof of the radionic connection between practitioner and patient in something called "radionic photography." This is where film that is never actually put in a camera, but is only exposed to the thoughts of the radionics practitioner, is then developed without applying light to the film. Radionic photography is a concrete example that thought (intention) is a form or function of torsion waves manifesting as light.

Radionic photography is a concrete example that thought (intention) is a form or function of torsion waves manifesting as light.

The matriarch of radionics, a chiropractor named Ruth Drown, created photographs of people at a distance by simply connecting with them mentally. She produced some uncanny images. In one she captured a fetus inside the womb of a patient who lived miles away. The shape of the fetus is clearly recognizable and the anatomy of the mother perfectly correct. Drown made other radionic photographs that were "taken" during surgeries happening sometimes hundreds of miles away that distinctly show surgical tools entering recognizable organs. These amazing images have been published in Tansley's *Radionics: Interface with the Ether Fields.*

Also a radionics practitioner, Tansley explains such remote energy transmission in terms of the "psi-field," described as a matrix in space filled with triangular energy vortices that allow for transmission and reception of intention or thought (torsion) energy between distant places. This takes us back to spiral standing waves that transcend time and space and is very much in keeping with the holographic model. Alternatively, Gariaev's research in the various healing applications of wave-genetics, which are often performed remotely, strongly supports the idea that DNA constitutes a "network" comparable to the Internet that, being present anywhere, is simultaneously present everywhere—effectively doing away with distance.

> *Gariaev's research in the various healing applications of wave-genetics, which are often performed remotely, strongly supports the idea that DNA constitutes a "network" comparable to the Internet that, being present anywhere, is simultaneously present everywhere—effectively doing away with distance.*

Biologist Rupert Sheldrake's Morphic Resonance theory posits a similar transpersonal "morphogenetic" network. Sheldrake's concept of "formative causation" emphasizes the existence of "morphic fields" that unite entire species universally outside space-time. According to Sheldrake, these omnipresent resonance fields can actually be expressed biologically if correctly tuned into—for example, through DNA—even if a species is extinct. Some readers may also be familiar with the notion of "noosphere," the name given by the great Jesuit philosopher Pierre Teilhard de Chardin to the field of mind and thought that encircles the planet and enables zeitgeist to happen: spontaneous transfer of ideas and technologies that suddenly seem to leap from consciousness to consciousness. Lynne McTaggart's popular book *The Field* provides yet another take on this nonlocal unifying fabric.

The final piece in the development of Potentiation Electromagnetic Repatterning fell into place when we were led to study the healing techniques of indigenous Hawaiian shamans known as *Kahunas*, who can miraculously heal people, often at a distance, using intoning. We learned that Kahunas, in order to transmit healing sounds to an ill person by proxy, use Earth's ley lines, which they call "aka threads"—a comprehensive network of sensitive "fiber-optic" graphite veins that seem almost designed to communicate between carbon-based life forms across distances.

In essence, Kahunas transmit sound through Earth while "triangulating" on the ill person with the light of their intention. It might even be said they generate an *energized narrative* sent to the recipient by sound and intention. This balanced use of telluric and astral energies almost certainly activates a self-healing potential in the individual's DNA, even though distance intervenes. Although Leigh and I have come to recognize that

Regenetics activations "travel" via the "information superhighway" of DNA, these concepts involving psi-fields and aka threads were very informative and inspirational.

Before returning from South America, we had the opportunity to test our theories about distance DNA activation and electromagnetic repatterning with approximately thirty people living in the United States. From that group we compiled our first list of fourteen testimonials that went for several pages. These testimonials included one spontaneous remission of a chronic rash; several cases of food allergies dramatically improving or disappearing; a shared sense of greater vitality; two reports of insomnia going away; and significant positive shifts in depression and fatigue.

Since then, while continuing to offer Potentiation to hundreds of clients, we have integrated two additional DNA activations—Articulation Bioenergy Enhancement and Elucidation Triune Activation—that round out the Regenetics Method. The results have been phenomenal, often surpassing our wildest expectations. This is especially the case when we receive enthusiastic feedback from clients living in different parts of the world whom we have never even met, as we regularly do.

You can probably imagine that Regenetics could be a challenging concept for many people today, that it might initially strike the more empirically minded as absurd. But like any revolutionary truth whose time has come, we believe that in the very near future the Regenetics Method, and similarly profound modalities based on emerging scientific principles supported by indisputable evidence, will be gradually acknowledged then universally accepted.

• PART II •
SACRED COSMOLOGY, SACRED BIOLOGY: THE REGENETICS METHOD & THE EVOLUTION OF CONSCIOUSNESS

9
The Shift in Human Consciousness

Are you aware that a Shift in human consciousness is occurring even as you read these words that employs celestial triggers such as supernovas and Earth's alignment with Galactic Center in the years leading up to 2012 to trigger the evolution of our species? This is perhaps why, consciously or otherwise, the Regenetics Method has piqued your interest.

This Shift has been documented in a stimulating multimedia presentation entitled "Preparing for the Shift," by Barry and Janae Weinhold, Ph.D.s. Over decades devoted to the study of consciousness and evolution, the Weinholds, both trained psychologists, have gathered overwhelming evidence that humanity is in the middle of a long-awaited Shift in consciousness predicted in hundreds of indigenous cultures all over the world.

Today this Shift is visible nearly every time you open a newspaper or turn on the TV. It can be seen in the breakdown of many old structures such as those that underpin governments, churches and corporations, as well as in families and individuals. It is also evident in the ecological breakdown of numerous Earth systems, a widespread perception time is accelerating, drastic changes in weather patterns, more people feeling overwhelmed by modern life's complexity, and increased polarization between groups, religions, and regions.

Fortunately, along with signs of breakdown, the Weinholds emphasize there is also considerable evidence of breakthrough: the appearance of stunningly gifted children in unprecedented numbers, the emergence of innovative and integrated healing modalities, people becoming less "religious" and more "spiritual," and the dawning of new communities and social structures based on servant leadership and other partnership principles.

Mayan timekeepers believe that human evolution unfolds as a result of precisely calibrated master cycles of time. They predict that Earth and humanity are about to be birthed into a new reality based on unity predicated on a dramatic advance in consciousness.

The significance of the winter solstice on December 21, 2012, according to the Mayan, Aztec, Incan and Hopi traditions, is that this date marks the close of several cycles of time.[11] The first is the end of the 26,000-year Mayan calendar, also called a "precession" and the *Annus Magnus* ("Great Year"), considered by many a gestational or birth cycle for Earth. Interestingly, the number 26,000 is very close to Plato's "ideal" number of 25,920. Mayan timekeepers believe that human evolution unfolds as a

---

[11] There is some spirited disagreement among scholars as to the exact date of the end of the so-called Mayan calendar. In *Maya Cosmogenesis 2012* John Major Jenkins has demonstrated that on December 21, 2012, Earth's "precessional" axis will be directly aligned with Galactic Center. Carl Johan Calleman proposes the alternative date of October 28, 2011, which could theoretically be more accurate based on evolutionary cycles as opposed to astronomical data. See *Solving the Greatest Mystery of Our Time: The Mayan Calendar*.

result of such precisely calibrated master cycles of time. They predict that Earth and humanity are about to be birthed into a new reality based on unity predicated on a dramatic advance in consciousness.

From a Mayan perspective, the Weinholds ask, "What began 26,000 years ago?" Their extensive psychohistorical research indicates this marked the beginning of humanity's psychological individuation. In human terms, becoming "individuated" means moving from being unconsciously united with the Creator or Ground of Being, to choosing to become divided from the Creator and developing separate individual consciousness, to finally returning to the Creator as conscious, aware individuals. Once people fully individuate, it becomes possible for them to make empowered, discerning choices and use intention to co-create reality with Source—or perhaps more accurately, to create reality *as* Source.

The second cycle of time ending in 2011 or 2012 highlighted in "Preparing for the Shift" is the close of the Galactic Year. It takes 225 million Earth years for the Milky Way Galaxy to make one complete rotation in the sky, which is believed to be a birth cycle for our galaxy (Figure 5). From a galactic perspective, the Weinholds ask, "What was conceived on Earth 225 million years ago?"

They point out this was when Earth's landmass, known as Pangaea, began separating into what we now know as the seven continents. This process of planetary individuation not only correlates with continental drift theory; as mentioned in Part I, there is also an energetic correspondence between Earth's twelve tectonic plates responsible for continental drift and the twelve pairs of cranial nerves in the human brain, which are themselves linked to the biblical Twelve Tribes. Considered together, this evidence suggests that Earth, like humans, has undergone her own "separating out" or individuation. Based on such interconnectedness, it is also reasonable to expect that as human consciousness exponentially increases, Earth will also undergo a significant—and observable—transformation.

Astronomers studying Galactic Center report that it periodically becomes extremely active. During these episodes, it spews out fierce barrages of cosmic energy equal to thousands of supernova explosions. These outbursts are the most energetic phenomenon in the known universe. A growing number of researchers such as Sergey Smelyakov, author of a fascinating paper entitled "The Auric Time Scale and the Mayan Factor," in addition to many indigenous peoples worldwide, theorize that as Galactic Center becomes more energized, it catalyzes human evolution through frequency emissions of torsion waves transmitted to Earth via the sun.

A comprehensive scientific model for the "Energetic Engine of Evolution" has been proposed by David Wilcock, a highly gifted psychic and speculative scientist whose theory of "Evolution as 'Intelligent Design'" deserves summarizing here. Citing the work of a vanguard of researchers including Tim Harwood, Glen Rein, Bruce Lipton, Richard Pasichnyk, Aleskey Dmitriev, Vladimir Poponin and Peter Gariaev, Wilcock presents a model that unites many disciplines and provides several critical missing pieces to the evolutionary puzzle. In his own words, this provocative model "suggests that humanity is on the verge of a near-spontaneous metamorphosis into a more highly evolved state of consciousness."

Basing his analysis on the realization, embraced by more and more of today's scientists, that Darwinian evolutionary theory is "extinct," Wilcock observes that the "probabilities that DNA could evolve by 'random mutation' are so minute as to be utterly laughable—akin to the idea that if you have enough monkeys tapping away on typewriters, one of them will eventually produce a complete Shakespearean play." Far surpassing the reach of gradual, incremental evolution, which certainly occurs as environmental *adaptation*, the fossil record from all over the planet makes it abundantly clear that species regularly *evolve* in heretofore inexplicable leaps and bounds, skipping what would seem from a Darwinian perspective to be crucial evolutionary phases. At the top of a long list of species whose evolution has baffled science is the human species.

Although for more than a century a "missing link" has been assumed to exist based on largely unchallenged Darwinian presumptions, scientists have never managed to discover it. "When we consider that the size of the brain literally doubled between that of humanity's apparent ancestors and ourselves, with no evidence of a smooth transformation whatsoever," writes Wilcock, "once again we see a spontaneous evolution of the creatures on Earth." One scientist associated with *National Geographic*, studying the intricate bone carvings dating to 70,000 B.C. found at Blombos Cave in South Africa, concluded that behavioral evolution mirrors anatomical development—an important observation meaning, in Wilcock's words, that "spontaneous evolution is not simply physiological, but consciousness-related as well. When a new bodily form has emerged, consciousness changes appear to occur."

Moreover, as indicated by the Mayan calendar, rather than in fits and starts, such evolutionary fast-forwards of physiology and consciousness happen in organized, predictable cycles. Theorizing a "harmonic relationship" between the 26,000-year Mayan calendar and 26-million-year period between extinctions/evolutionary leaps in the fossil record, Wilcock notes that all Earth species have suddenly evolved, or metamorphosed, every 26 million years, making a strong case for "an outside energetic influence that operates in a regular, cyclic fashion."

To answer the question what outside energetic influence is responsible for these rhythmic evolutionary revolutions, it is necessary to factor in the concept of torsion energy introduced in Part I. Some writers, most notably Barbara Hand Clow, have focused attention on something called the Photon Belt or Photon Band, which can be envisioned as a torsion-wave "light lattice" connecting Earth via our sun to Galactic Center that serves as a guiding data communication network for human and planetary evolution.

While some astronomers have scoffed at the notion of a Photon Band, other scientists who grasp the higher-dimensional nature of this network's light understand that it not only exists but plays a critical role in cosmic evolution. In 1962, writes Ron Radhoff in *New Science News*, the year many

> say we entered the Aquarian Age, we began to enter into the influence of [the] photon-belt ... We will pass into

Figure 5: The Photon Band & Black Road
It takes 225 million Earth years for the Milky Way Galaxy to make one complete rotation through the Photon Band, which is believed to be a birth cycle for our galaxy. The Black Road can be conceptualized as simultaneously an astrophysical and genetic alignment with Galactic Center that engenders a Shift in consciousness, allowing humanity to return "home."

the center of it by the year 2011 ... St. Germain refers to the photon-belt as the Golden Nebula, a parallel universe of much higher vibration. Little by little it is absorbing our universe. As we merge with this higher vibration universe, it will become the catalyst for massive changes.

Wilcock's research indicates that something very much like a Photon Band most definitely exists as lines of higher-dimensional torsion radiation emanating from Galactic Center. Both Wilcock and Clow envision the Photon Band as tracing figure-eights throughout the spiraling pattern of the Milky Way Galaxy (Figure 5). It appears from Dr. Nikolai Kozyrev's research involving aether also mentioned in Part I that such looping energy based on the phi ratio (1.6180339) is, among other things, directly responsible for our cyclical experience of time.

Recalling the aether theories of Kozyrev, fellow Russian scientist Sergey Smelyakov's research demonstrates that the harmonic vibrations of phi, also referred to as the Golden Mean and Fibonacci sequence, inform the very fabric of space-time. Mathematically, the Photon Band appears to be structured on phi, producing set cosmic intervals the Mayans were aware of when constructing their uncannily accurate calendar. Smelyakov's "The Auric Time Scale and the Mayan Factor" compellingly suggests that Earth connects to Galactic Center via our solar system in a harmonic fashion he calls "Solar-planetary Synchronism," a vibratory relationship based on the Golden Mean.

In an article entitled "The Ultimate Secret of the Mayan Calendar," Wilcock cites Smelyakov's research, writing that it helps explain the end of the Mayan calendar in geometric terms as an "infinitely-converging end point" in which time appears to "collapse." This is because time as we experience it follows the imploding spirals of phi much like a finger tracing the cyclical involutions of a conch shell to its centerpoint. History, then, does not exactly repeat itself; it is more like climbing a spiral staircase. While Terrence McKenna's controversial "Timewave Zero" theory has many similarities to Smelyakov's Solar-planetary Synchronism, the latter appears more internally consistent and scientifically sound.

Torsion energy spiraling as the Photon Band from the creative consciousness at the Core of our universe is Wilcock's "Energetic Engine of Evolution." Because of its curvilinear form, the Photon Band is composed of swaths of lesser and greater density of torsion waves manifesting as higher-dimensional light. As our solar system orbits episodically into galactic regions characterized by greater density of torsion waves (i.e., greater light or consciousness), which it is currently doing, life on our planet, including the living organism that is Earth, is intelligently stimulated to evolve in spectacular ways not only physically but also mentally, emotionally, and spiritually.

As our solar system orbits into galactic regions characterized by greater density of torsion waves (i.e., greater light or consciousness), which it is currently doing, life on our planet, including the living organism that is Earth, is intelligently stimulated to evolve in spectacular ways not only physically but also mentally, emotionally, and spiritually.

"By combining the effects of geo-cosmic change with the overall flourishing of humanity in the cultural and spiritual sense," observes Wilcock, "we see that as the cycle continues to exponentially accelerate its energetic rate of vibration into the 2012-2013 'singularity,' we can expect ... rapid increases in human awareness." This centripetal cycle leads inexorably to a "discontinuous mega-event where 'time and space collapse.'" Perhaps this transformation of our experience of time and space is the truth behind the disjointed description of the "end of days" in the Book of Revelation.

In humans, evolutionary activation occurs as torsion waves stimulate potential DNA's transposons to rewrite the genetic code—a phenomenon supported by a considerable amount of scientific evidence. Bruce Lipton's research unambiguously affirms that cells possess the ability to reprogram their own DNA, with measurable physical results such as otherwise inexplicable dietary modifications in organisms, when environmentally prompted. Dr. Lipton hypothesizes that such rewriting, which is typically beneficial, accounts for up to ninety-eight percent of evolutionary transformation.

Similarly, in a concise but excellent study entitled "Retrotransposons as Engines of Human Bodily Transformation," biochemist Colm Kelleher addresses the subject of radical genetic adaptation or evolution as a result of what he terms a "transposition burst." "If one were to hypothesize a transmutation of the human body," writes Dr. Kelleher, it

> would be necessary to orchestrate a change, cell by cell, involving the simultaneous silencing of hundreds of genes and the activation of a different set of hundreds more. A transposition burst is a plausible mechanism at

the DNA/RNA level that could accomplish such a genome wide change. Transposition bursts comprise the concerted movement of multiple mobile DNA elements from different genetic locations to new positions, sometimes on different chromosomes ... Human DNA contains an abundance of the necessary genetic structures to accomplish a transposition burst involving hundreds, or even thousands, of genes.

Referencing a particular DNA sequence containing three different transposon families (a genetic trinity) arranged in beadlike formation, Kelleher theorizes that owing to its tripartite configuration, this DNA sequence would be "an effective participant in large scale transposon mediated genetic change that eventually results in transformation of the human body."

Perhaps the most undeniable evidence supporting the concept of a torsion life-wave or Photon Band of universal creative consciousness energetically directing the spontaneous formation and development of Earth species comes from Tim Harwood, who calls attention to one of nature's more miraculous phenomena. After caterpillars form their chrysalis during metamorphosis, it is a little-known but very relevant fact that they completely dissolve into a soup of amino acids before reassembling into butterflies. This soup contains no recognizable cells or DNA as it is currently understood, but when the time is right, the torsion life-wave signals the DNA to recombine and, within a matter of days, cells emerge to create new life-forms.

Wilcock concludes that the human species, somewhat like caterpillars entering metamorphosis, is currently "being programmed by the galactic center to

become more advanced while ... still here in our bodies."
This is made possible because the

> DNA molecule is like a programmable piece of hardware
> ... so that if you change the energy wave that moves
> through it, the jumping DNA will encode it into a
> completely different form. It is therefore possible that as
> we move into increasingly "intelligent" zones of energy
> in the galaxy, the DNA energy patterns for the creatures
> on the planet are all upgraded, and the mutations occur
> so rapidly—well within one lifetime—that no
> "transitional" fossils exist.

Earth's movement through a denser area of the
Photon Band directly aligned with Galactic Center began
around the time of the so-called Harmonic Convergence in
1987, will enter into a historical astronomical alignment
around 2012, and will be complete (from our present
linear perspective) by about 2016. Over the course of the
past two decades, as Wilcock and the Weinholds point out,
major Earth, planetary and solar changes—from
unprecedented alterations in planetary atmospheres to
drastic surges in volcanic and earthquake activity—have
been observed. Arguably of greatest significance from our
perspective is that the sun is now moving into alignment
with Galactic Center. During this transit the sun's
magnetic field has increased over 230% and there have
been wildly elevated levels of sunspot activity (as reported
by NASA and other space agencies) that have transmitted
record-breaking waves of electromagnetic (to say nothing
of torsion) energy to Earth and, thus, to us.

It is worth noting we are composed of the same
substances found in the heavens, so it really is not so odd
that celestial events should profoundly impact us. Harvard

professor of astronomy Robert Kirshner has remarked that "supernovas created the elements we take for granted—the oxygen we breathe, the calcium in our bones, and the iron in our blood are products of the stars."[12] Other researchers, observing that most of DNA's amino acids are also found in space, have hypothesized that DNA actually came from space—an increasingly popular theory known as "Panspermia."

Fascinatingly, Fritz Albert Popp's research in biophotons describes the dying process of cells as virtually identical to that of stars. Just before dying, cells transform into "supernovas" as the light they emit increases in intensity a thousand times before being suddenly extinguished. On a related note, and just as extraordinarily, Galactic Center, our point of origin, is located in the constellation Ophiuchus, "the serpent bearer," an obvious reference to the spiraling, serpentine helixes of DNA. Here, in ancient symbolism, we find a direct link between the creational torsion waves emitted by Galactic Center and the DNA molecule to which, by all indications, they give rise.

The Vedics were well aware of such an ener-genetic connection between Galactic Center and DNA as well as of the many cycles of time ending around 2012, employing the term *somvarta* to describe the intelligent waves of Core energy responsible for the spontaneous evolution of species. Another ancient concept, the Golden Mean, precisely defines the mathematical relationship between "above" and "below." The DNA molecule is minutely structured on phi or the Golden Mean, measuring 34 x 21 angstroms for each full helical spiral. Concordantly, the

---

[12] Quoted in William Henry, *The Healing Sun Code.*

average mean orbit of each of the planets moving away from the sun is also a Fibonacci sequence that translates to almost exactly 1.6180339.

10
Unconditional Love, Torsion Energy & Human Evolution

A second point related to human evolution that needs emphasizing is that the Shift now occurring is directly related to an increase in cosmic consciousness based in unconditional love. The Shift may be visualized as simultaneously evolution, revolution and, to borrow a term from the Weinholds, "LOVEvolution™."

Clairvoyance is unnecessary to see that human consciousness is expanding at a tremendous rate. A trip to the local bookstore demonstrates that consciousness, along with associated terms such as "intention" and "manifestation," has become a cultural buzz word. Nor is this exponentially increasing focus on consciousness merely a "new age" phenomenon. Relatively mainstream books such as Michael Talbot's *The Holographic Universe* and Dr. Larry Dossey's *Reinventing Medicine* make a clear and compelling case that science is beginning to admit the ancient hermetic principle that Mind is reality's primary building block.

On this subject, renowned psychiatrist Stanislov Grof has written that "modern consciousness research reveals that our psyches have no real or absolute boundaries; on the contrary, we are part of an infinite field of consciousness that encompasses all there is—

beyond space-time and into realities we have yet to explore." Such an expansive view of consciousness also informs Leonard Horowitz's review of the science of quantum holography, where he reminds us not only that a unified field of consciousness exists but also that it "may be explained as emerging from a previously overlooked physical vacuum or energy matrix." From a human perspective, this nonlocal energy field functions through quantum connections between DNA and universal creative consciousness or torsion energy.

For some, the current global blossoming of consciousness is viewed as a natural process of human evolution. To others, this phenomenon appears more radical, a spontaneous genetic leap forward. Still others believe that this step is merely the bringing forth of what has always existed as a human potential: a revolution back in the direction of wholeness and integration. I trust by now the reader understands that these ways of envisioning our species' present evolutionary phase are by no means mutually exclusive.

For the Mayans, Mastery of Intention corresponded to a unity consciousness that would infuse biology itself with new structures and possibilities quite outside the box of even much of today's "advanced" thinking about human bio-spiritual potential.

As the term *LOVEvolution* ™ suggests, many believe that the dawning Age of Light or Age of Consciousness defines itself in relation to our capacity for unconditional love, our ability to transcend enemy patterning and victim consciousness while adopting unity consciousness that sees divinity in all things. From this standpoint, it might be said humans are evolving into a "biologically conscious" species capable of holding and sharing the full light of unconditional love.

Long ago the Mayans conceptualized this ultimate evolutionary stage that would occur in the years leading up to 2012 as Mastery of Intention. For the Mayans, Mastery of Intention corresponded to a unity consciousness that would infuse biology itself with new structures and possibilities quite outside the box of even much of today's "advanced" thinking about human bio-spiritual potential. According to Joseph Chilton Pearce in *The Biology of Transcendence*, "Transcendence is our biological imperative, a state we have been moving toward for millennia." The title of another excellent study by Pearce neatly summarizes the name of the endgame we are now playing: *Evolution's End: Claiming the Potential of Our Intelligence*.

How does one master intention in order to claim this potential? How does one consciously evolve into transcendence? In other words, how can we use consciousness to facilitate our own metamorphosis? The previously cited research by Bruce Lipton proves that consciousness can reprogram DNA. Our discussion of this topic in the last chapter centered on galactic consciousness, torsion waves spurring human evolution as Earth moves into a denser or brighter area of the Photon Band. But what role does an individual's consciousness play in this cosmic drama of becoming?

Here it is my pleasure to touch briefly on the genetic studies performed by cell biologist Glen Rein. In this important research that deserves further exploration, DNA inside human cells was observed in order to determine the impact of emotions on genetic material as well as expression. Dr. Rein discovered that anger, fear and similar emotions have the power to contract the DNA molecule, literally compressing it like an accordion. On the other hand, emotions such as joy, gratitude and love unwind or decompress DNA exposed to them. Similar conclusions had already been reached by other researchers including Dan Winter, but to the best of my knowledge, Rein is the first to offer experimental proof of DNA's ability to contract and expand when emotionally prompted.

Rein's research makes a direct connection between torsion energy and life-affirming emotions, particularly unconditional love, indicating that the latter literally propels evolution. Only the love-based emotions stimulate DNA to decompress so that messenger RNA can access codes for healing.

These findings can help us answer the critical question of how to participate consciously in our own evolution in a very specific manner. Rein's research makes a direct connection between torsion energy and life-affirming emotions, particularly unconditional love, indicating that the latter literally propels evolution. Only the love-based emotions stimulate DNA to decompress so that messenger RNA can access codes for healing. Hatred, depression, boredom and the like cause DNA to close down on itself, severely limiting access to genetic information necessary for healing as well as evolution.

In keeping with Rein's research, Barbara Marciniak in *Path of Empowerment* writes that "genuine feelings of love and appreciation for your body convey a positive message containing essential life-sustaining signals that result in excellent health." In direct contrast, maintaining "feelings of doom and despair, loneliness, helplessness, denial, anger, resentment, jealousy, greed, and fear conveys a negative message that promotes discord within the physical functions of the body." Marciniak concludes that the "ability to both give and receive love ... holds the true key to healing because it is the most life-sustaining and affirming form of emotional expression."

Rein's brilliant research, supported by Marciniak's inspired keys for surviving and thriving in a chaotic world in the process of transformation, indicates that *the single most important factor in our personal evolution is our commitment to open ourselves to our own healing by giving and receiving the primary torsion wave known as unconditional love.*

Appropriately, Wilcock's evolutionary model is crystal clear on the point that Earth and humans are evolving from a logos anchored in the third dimension to an existence rooted in fourth-dimensional, heart-based consciousness. In *The Biology of Transcendence* Pearce advances a hypothesis supporting this radical assertion based on the little-known fact that humans actually possess four neural centers in addition to the brain. One of these, currently in a state of development, is the "brain" located in and around the heart. Not surprisingly, the fourth or "heart" chakra, which is linked to the fourth dimension in the Regenetics model, is typically associated with Christ consciousness or unconditional love.

It is crucial that we understand the evolutionary engine behind this momentous developmental stage for our species, unconditional love, not as a weak abstraction but as an omnipotent creational force of torsion energy that birthed—as it is still birthing—everything in the multiverse, including ourselves. Unconditional love is aptly named because the creative principle of love places no conditions on its creations, allowing for the exercise of free will in the karmic cycle of evolving human consciousness. The Bible sums up this foundational concept in three words: *God is love*. For the ancient Egyptians and Mayans, to cite but two examples, such infinite love associated with the life-giving feminine principle emanates from Galactic Center, also called the Central or Healing Sun.

Today this Core of our galaxy is thought by most scientists to be a black hole of massive proportions: the equivalent of as many as 4 million of our suns. For decades it was believed black holes destroy everything that falls into them. Recently, however, physicist Stephen Hawking performed an abrupt about-face when he was quoted by an online news source (http://www.rense.com) as saying, "It seems that black holes may after all allow information within them to escape." If we understand "information" to include higher-dimensional torsion-wave codes that create and modify life such as those that find expression via transposons in potential DNA, life may indeed, as whole civilizations of ancients claimed, originate from black holes.

The crisis, as well as the opportunity, of our time is to surrender our ego and conditioned fear mechanisms to the primary torsion energy of unconditional love that is seeking to evolve us and is calling us as a species home.

Alternatively, it is possible that Galactic Center contains not only a black hole but also a "white hole." In the words of investigative mythologist William Henry, "Of all the high-energy photons beamed at us by the Core, probably none are more puzzling than those emitted in gamma ray bursts. Astrophysicists speculate these bursts are coming from a white hole, a 'cosmic gusher' of matter and energy ... [W]hatever a black hole can devour, a *white hole* can spit out. These white holes precisely conform to the image the ancients held of the center of our galaxy."

In Chinese the character for "crisis" also means "opportunity." "Within a larger framework of reality," writes Marciniak, "a crisis can be thought of as a meeting of minds at the crossroads of opportunity—a juncture where you recognize exactly where you are and consciously choose the best possible outcome for where you are going." The crisis, as well as the opportunity, of our time is to surrender our ego and conditioned fear mechanisms to the primary torsion energy of unconditional love that is seeking to evolve us and is calling us as a species home.

This "home" may be simply a state of awareness that transcends duality and consciously exists in a multidimensional continuum. Wilcock sees "returning home" as a dimensional Shift referred to in the Bible as "ascension," in this case envisioned as a spontaneous metamorphosis or transmutation involving both consciousness and biology similar to what happened to Jesus in the Resurrection. "There is a parallel in the Shroud of Turin," Wilcock notes, "where certain researchers have found that Jesus' body burned a complete three-dimensional image of itself into the cloth." Through experimentation it was determined that "such a burn could only be caused by an instantaneous blast at a very high temperature, 'zapping' the cloth like an X-ray."

Others also visualize returning home in terms of a radical Shift. Barbara Hand Clow has remarked that, in the final analysis, all dilemmas are perceptual—which implies that all solutions are perceptual as well. This sentiment is echoed by Judith Bluestone Polich in *Return of the Children of Light*, where humanity is described as standing on the brink of a collective perceptual "awakening. As the cosmic cycles of time are telling us, it is the time for a major turn upon the spiral path of evolving human consciousness, when the light that has descended into matter begins the ascent back to its origin."

The preceding quote also suggests that the home to which we have been referring may indicate some other place entirely. The 2012 alignment of the December solstice sun with Galactic Center creates what some ancients called the Black Road (Figure 5). It is conceivable we are meant to follow the Black Road home to our "transdimensional" Source, where we experience a state of being that altogether transcends this holographic reality composed of various "frequency domains" or dimensions. After all, a white hole is basically a black hole reversed. The two are thought to meet at their small ends like a pair of funnels. It is mathematically possible to enter a black hole and emerge from a white hole in a completely new universe.[13]

---

[13] Something very similar happens to Jodie Foster's character in the movie *Contact*, based on the novel by the same name by world-famous astronomer Carl Sagan. The concept of the Black Road is supported by some compelling speculative cosmology that has found its way into the mainstream.

11
Becoming Light

It must also be stressed that the evolution of consciousness and physiology we are presently embarking on as a species involves a positive genetic (trans)mutation that empowers humans to expand their multidimensional awareness while, effectively, becoming light.

Everything is energy. Einstein definitively established this with his famous theorem E=MC², which proved the interchangeability of matter and energy. Concerning matter, Einstein once remarked, "we have been all wrong. What we have called matter is energy, whose vibration has been so lowered as to be perceptible to the senses. There is no matter." Arguably, this truth that has now been validated by the quantum sciences was known to the ancient Hindus when they employed the term *maya*, meaning the illusion often mistaken for reality. Without a doubt, vanguard Russian scientists such as Kozyrev, Gariaev and Poponin who have studied torsion waves understand that energy (including so-called matter) is consciousness, and vice versa.

The notion that everything is energy or consciousness directly applies to human biology. The materialistic, "Era I" view of the body as a machine that may run on energy but is somehow distinguishable from it is fast giving way to undeniable evidence that we, too, at our most fundamental level, are manifestations of conscious energy. The holographic model, to reiterate, views the ostensibly physical universe in terms of intersecting electromagnetic frequencies that, in effect, project the staggering illusions we think of as the world ... and ourselves. "When two waves [for example, sound and light] come together they interact with each other producing [a hologram]," writes Horowitz. "Information is processed and cell structures are organized by these forces including the structure and standing waves created by DNA."

The notion that everything is energy or consciousness directly applies to human biology. The materialistic, "Era I" view of the body as a machine that may run on energy but is somehow distinguishable from it is fast giving way to undeniable evidence that we, too, are conscious energy.

By now it should not strike the reader as unreasonable to learn that in *Vibrational Medicine*, Dr. Richard Gerber concludes that matter, including human cells, is actually "frozen light." Horowitz reaches precisely the same conclusion, bluntly stating that humans are "crystallized or precipitated light." This assertion is consistent not only with torsion-wave research and the holographic model but with the findings of more mainstream quantum physics, which has demonstrated that light (much like DNA) is capable of both carrying and remembering data.

The concept of light as information, or "light in formation," is an old one that has for centuries found expression in various types of sacred geometry. Others have suggested that angels, often depicted as divine messengers, are really *angles* or rays of light that convey information (typically experienced as "inspiration") from a celestial source. This expanded conception of light as a form of consciousness underpins, for example, the Toltec worldview of Don Miguel Ruiz, medical doctor, shaman and bestselling author of *The Four Agreements,* whose cosmology includes the Photon Band as a connector between Galactic Center and our sun. With the latter being Earth's primary source of light or information, the reverence for the sun in virtually all pre-industrialized cultures appears not naïve but an informed and deliberate focus on humanity's local source of universal creative consciousness.

New neurological research indicates that humans' tremendous brainpower, even operating below ten percent of our capacity, results not just from biochemistry but from the brain's impressive ability to function as a holographic data storage and retrieval system (a "hard-drive") that employs different light angles to read information ("software"). This implies, as noted, that the brain is a sophisticated holographic biocomputer that operates through electromagnetic frequencies. Not surprisingly, DNA has been shown to function very similarly. Human biology may thus be considered electromagnetic at the level of its manifestation from the torsion life-wave that sustains it. As Deepak Chopra has observed, human cells, far from being merely functional vessels, are in actuality electromagnetic fields of possibility and potential.

Human electromagnetic frequencies can be clearly identified in the aura. As detailed in Part I, it is now generally agreed that humans possess a detectable aura. Kirlian photography has captured this iridescent halo around the body for decades; and recently, Dr. Valerie

Hunt, UCLA professor and author of *Infinite Mind*, has even measured the human aura with an EEG machine. Early in the 20th Century, it was theorized that the aura comprises various electromagnetic frequency bands known as auric fields, and that each of these governs distinct aspects of human biology, psychology, and spirituality.

Each electromagnetic field also corresponds to, and interfaces with, a specific dimension. The third field, for instance, is keyed to the third dimension. The electromagnetic fields can be thought of as a geometric matrix, a "Jacob's ladder" that allows access to increasingly subtle frequency domains. This unfolding of perception to the full range represented by the auric fields and corresponding chakras is what it means to become "multidimensional." It is believed by Wilcock, myself and others that eight dimensions (not counting the "transdimension" of Source) are available to human perception at our present evolutionary stage, which means that operating in the first three dimensions, as most people do, humans currently only access just over a third of "reality." This does not even take into account the probable existence of multiple parallel realities.

The electromagnetic fields can be thought of as a geometric matrix, a "Jacob's ladder" that allows access to increasingly subtle frequency domains. This unfolding of perception to the full range represented by the auric fields and corresponding chakras is what it means to become "multidimensional."

According to Gregg Braden in *The God Code*, also noted, the ancient Hebrew four-letter name for God is secretly code for DNA based on the genetic code's chemical composition. "Applying this discovery to the language of life," writes Braden, "the familiar elements of hydrogen, nitrogen, oxygen, and carbon that form our DNA may now be replaced with key letters ... In so doing, the code of life is transformed into the words of a timeless message [that] reads: '*God/Eternal within the body.*'" If God is indeed in the body—and consciousness and physiology are, from an evolutionary perspective, inextricably linked—we must acknowledge that *divine consciousness is available in and through physicality.*

One intriguing aspect of DNA is that most people utilize only about ten—some say as little as three—percent of it. As previously remarked, the other ninety percent or more has been dismissed by mainstream genetic science as "junk." Interestingly, the fact that we use at best ten percent of our DNA correlates to the fact that we use at most ten percent of our brain. Still more provocative is that, according to one of the latest scientific models, String theory, less than ten percent of the matter in the universe is visible. The other ninety percent or so is sometimes called "dark matter" and may very well, given the nonlocal quality of the torsion energy at its base, reside in other dimensions.

Could "junk" DNA truly have biologically transformative potential awaiting activation? Could it somehow activate the unused portion of the human brain? Could this brain activation succeed in opening our godlike perceptual faculties, allowing us to climb the "multidimensional ladder" of our electromagnetic fields and experience the invisible ninety percent of the universe? Following the time-honored wisdom of "As above, so below," could reports that these perceptual faculties are indeed emerging in many people, especially today's extraordinarily gifted children, have anything to do with an increase in torsion energy in the form of superluminal light emanating from Galactic Center?

Many believe the answer to all these questions is an emphatic *yes*. According to William Henry, physicists "have established that a vast cosmic ocean of quintessence ... invisible to our telescopes ... surrounds the visible galaxies. If they are right, this 'dark matter' ... that composes [what] we ... see 'out there' is also 'in here' ... This implies that 9/10 of ourselves is also unknown."

Braden, who began his career as a geological scientist, was one of the first from the scientific community to theorize, based largely on observable Earth changes, that our planet is experiencing some type of frequency increase that will ultimately activate the dormant potential of our DNA. As detailed in *Awakening to Zero Point*, this evolutionary activation, or "Collective Initiation," possibly relates to Earth's harmonic frequency, known as the Schumann resonance. Although this is a scientifically controversial subject and has yet to be adequately substantiated, a number of researchers, including myself, still believe that some, possibly higher-dimensional (torsion) aspect of Earth's resonance is indeed increasing in keeping with the evolutionary timeline encoded in the Mayan calendar. Perhaps new data will facilitate our collective understanding.

Braden argues that Earth's hypothetical frequency increase, possibly linked to denser or brighter "light information" stemming from increased celestial activity, will result in new combinations of amino acids—in

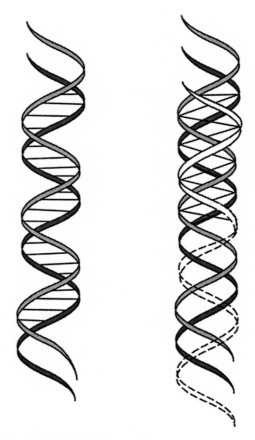

Figure 6: From Biology to Triology
The above illustration shows how a third strand of DNA might interface with and modify the existing double helix. Both as a possible biological reality and as a metaphor for activating the latent intelligence in potential DNA, the triple helix is genetically consistent with the movement away from a binary or dualistic "operating system" in favor of a trinitized or "trinary" code capable of engendering an evolutionary Shift into unity consciousness. Note how the geometry of three strands naturally produces interlocking tetrahedral shapes suggestive of molecular *merkabahs*.

essence, new DNA. From a genetics perspective, this is tantamount to saying that a new life-form is emerging out of the human species. As we have already seen, this is not nearly as odd as it may at first sound, given DNA's spectacular capacity for adaptive mutation. Recently, the phrase "quantum biology" has appeared in response (in some cases) to allegedly suppressed evidence suggesting that a third strand of DNA is currently activating in humans, forming what may be a "triple helix." I believe the creation of a third strand of DNA is a reality; however, even as a metaphor for evolving the latent intelligence of our existing DNA, the notion of a third helix has a certain conceptual value (Figure 6).

On the subject of the emergence of a new genotype of human, Judith Polich writes that "the codes to awakening our ancestral endowment—namely, our inner light—may lie hidden within the structure of our DNA." As we individually "begin to remember who we are, a new consciousness will emerge. [As] soon as this revisioning reaches a critical mass, it will trigger an evolutionary leap to a new human species—the long-awaited, quantumly endowed spiritual human known to ancient cultures as the child of light."

All living beings emit light. Anticipating the latest Russian research in wave-genetics, in the 1920s another Russian scientist, Alexander Gurvich, pioneered the concept of light frequency signaling via "mitogenic rays" in human cells. At about the same time in Germany, Marco Bischof published an influential text entitled *Biophotons: The Light in Our Cells*. By 1974 German biophysicist Fritz Albert Popp's biophoton theory had confirmed the basic mitogenic hypothesis, demonstrating that DNA is the source of bioluminescence. Popp's theory, in turn, was confirmed by Herbert Froehlich and Nobel laureate Ilya Prigogine.

In biology circles more and more attention is now being paid to a system known as "biophoton light communication" that appears essential to many regulatory processes in living organisms. The cellular hologram equivalent of the nervous system, this intricate communication network that employs light for data transfer operates far more quickly than the nervous system and may be considered a real-time (parallel-processing) quantum biocomputer allowing for an unmediated electromagnetic interface with the individual's environment.[14]

Biologist Rupert Sheldrake's Morphic Resonance theory strongly suggests that cellular bioluminescence (which in humans ranges from ultraviolet to infrared) is both personal and transpersonal. In other words, not only is the individual human "networked" with DNA light emitters and receptors; it appears our entire species is morphogenetically networked much like individual cells that form a larger biological entity: humanity. This assertion has been substantiated by the Gariaev group, whose findings liken DNA not just to a holographic biocomputer but to a "biological Internet" that links all human beings. Many native wisdom traditions are based on an equivalent understanding of the universe (human

---

[14] This interface, I contend, occurs at the level of the electromagnetic fields, the "mind," by way of the genetic sound-light translation mechanism described in Chapter Six. Rather than biophoton light communication, perhaps a more accurate name for this data transfer system, one that respects the primacy of sound at the ener-genetic level, would be "biophonon-photon communication."

inhabitants included) as a single living being intelligently networked like a biological organism.

"Eastern teachings tell us that the living light is encoded in our form," writes Polich. "The ancient concept of the macrocosm as microcosm ... tells us that the greater divine [light] is reflected in the human body. Expressed in another manner, this means that ... the spiritual human ... has encoded within it a divine blueprint." This divine blueprint, which Polich refers to following the kabalistic tradition as the Adam Kadmon, is also called the *lightbody*. The lightbody (also known as the soul body) is no esoteric concept but a biological reality, one that gives rise to a radically new "spiritual" biochemistry and genetics that allow for the incarnation of the full light of unity consciousness in every cell of the body.

The lightbody begins to express itself when dormant potential DNA codes are keyed by torsion energy, particularly sound and intention spiral standing waves of a higher-dimensional nature derived from the primary torsion energy of unconditional love, such that our cells begin to recognize light as an energy source and metabolize it somewhat like plants do in photosynthesis.

The lightbody begins to express itself when dormant potential DNA codes are keyed by torsion energy, particularly *sound* and *intention* spiral standing waves of a higher-dimensional nature derived from the primary torsion energy of unconditional love, such that our cells begin to recognize light as an energy source and metabolize it somewhat like plants do in photosynthesis. I am specifically referring to the invisible (superluminal) torsion light emitted by the Healing Sun and transmitted to us from Galactic Center outside space-time by way of the Photon Band and our sun. Among other benefits, this cellular evolution is capable of significantly increasing

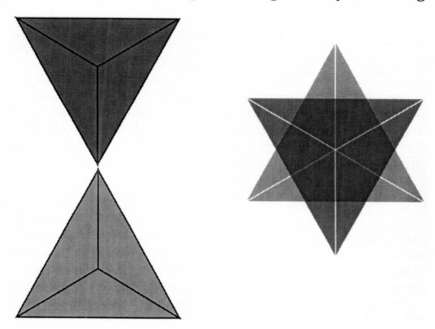

Figure 7: Tetrahedron & *Merkabah*
Note how from a three-dimensional perspective, the merkabah is an interface between a downward-pointing tetrahedron and an upward-pointing one, creating a molecular marriage between "above" and "below." It is also interesting to remark the similarity between this convergence and that of the theoretically funnel-shaped black and white holes approaching each other at Galactic Center.

metabolism—encouraging detoxification, rehydration and, ultimately, regeneration.[15]

In this profoundly transformational process, the liquid crystals of cells evolve from primitive hexagonal structures observed in normal human tissues to what have been called "stellar" tetrahedrons. This structural change is extremely consequential. The hydrogen bond angles of our water molecules literally broaden and become interlocking tetrahedrons in order to hold more light or photonic energy that partially results from the expanded hydrogen bonds themselves. These structures that form the liquid matrix for the new blood and tissues resemble three-dimensional Stars of David or molecular *merkabahs*. Merkabah is an ancient kabalistic word meaning "chariot of light" (Figures 6 and 7).

This helps explain the confusion that has often surrounded the merkabah, which has sometimes been taken to denote a type of spaceship. The irony is that the merkabah is a sort of spaceship—and that this spaceship is the individual's genetically activated lightbody. According to Barbara Marciniak, the merkabah "represents the figure of the human being in its most unlimited state—the totally free human ... The lightbody is the body that holds the complete mutation of the species. It [can] juggle realities through the shifting of consciousness by intent" like changing channels on a television. In a similar vein, Tashíra Tachí-ren describes the merkabah as a "crystalline

---

[15] On a related subject, Horowitz cites evidence that phototherapies (including sunlight) may "1) change [cell] membrane permeability; 2) increase cellular nutrient and mineral entry into the cell, and 3) facilitate release of toxins from the membrane and cell interior."

Light structure that allows you to pass through space, time, and dimensions, completely in your totality."

The lightbody results from and operates through embodied higher light or consciousness. It represents the natural result of a perceptual evolution into enlightenment that is, by many indications, occurring on a planetary level. From this perspective, there is perhaps no such thing as ascension, only "descension" of the light of soul into physical form. The lightbody may also be, literally, the spaceship that allows us to travel the multi- and transdimensional Black Road through the stars. Tachí-ren sees "going to Lightbody [as] only a part of a much larger process [in which] all planes and dimensions [merge] back into the Source for this universe, which then merges with other Source-systems, and so on, back to the One." However we define returning home, the lightbody is the vehicle that takes us there.

12
DNA Activation & Enlightenment

A variety of techniques exist to facilitate adaptation to new forms of thought and their corresponding biological structures or "thought-forms." Over the centuries, hundreds of modalities have been developed to assist in unfolding the spiritual human (the "Holy Grail") that exists as a genetic potential in everyone. Alchemy is an excellent example from antiquity. Etymologically, *alchemy* derives from the Arabic *al* (the) and *khame* (blackness) and might be defined as the science of creating light out of darkness. As students of this discipline eventually discover, alchemy's real goal is not to turn lead to gold but to transform human biology into a physiology of golden light. Stated a bit differently, alchemy's primary objective is enlightenment, or creation of the lightbody.

Today many more lightbody activation techniques are being made available, which itself signifies a significant movement toward global bio-spiritual enlightenment. Leigh and I have been fortunate enough to develop one such method. Regenetics employs specific combinations of sound and intention, which are differentiated aspects of the primary torsion energy of unconditional love, to stimulate the latent potential in DNA designed to facilitate the evolution of human beings into unity consciousness and its corresponding physiology of light.

DNA, as Braden points out in *The God Code*, is by its very sacredly encoded nature a unifying principle for humanity—one capable of bringing peace and harmony to the Twelve Tribes of a planetary population faced with a decision between succumbing to crisis or embracing opportunity. "The discovery of God's name within our bodies shows us the benefit of merging different ways of knowing into a single understanding," he writes. "By crossing the traditional boundaries that define chemistry, language, history, and religion, we are shown the power of a larger, integrated worldview." That we can activate DNA to expand our worldview and, in the process, evolve a biology based on unity consciousness is truly a divine gift at this crossroads in history when, to quote Barbara Marx Hubbard, we must "decide between conscious evolution, or extinction through misuse of our powers."

Through harmonic resonance, Potentiation establishes a clearer connection with the unconditional love frequency emanating as higher-dimensional spiral standing waves of sound and light from the Healing Sun at Galactic Center. In other words, Potentiation attunes DNA to the primary torsion energy of Source.

The Regenetics Method features three integrated DNA activations that collectively establish the energenetic precondition for unfoldment of the lightbody. The first of these, Potentiation, activates DNA to repattern the body's electromagnetic fields, resetting the human bioenergy blueprint to an infinity circuit as detailed in Part I. DNA has been compared to an antenna connecting humanity to Source whose reception can be clouded by toxicity and trauma. Potentiation activates DNA to begin removing this toxicity and trauma, establishing a clearer connection through harmonic resonance with the unconditional love frequency emanating as higher-dimensional spiral standing waves of sound and light from the Healing Sun at Galactic Center. In other words, Potentiation attunes DNA to the primary torsion energy of Source.

As mentioned, Leigh and I consider ourselves merely facilitators for the individual's own bio-spiritual unfoldment. We actually heal ourselves. This is an important point that can hardly be overemphasized. As William Henry reminds us, the "Healing Sun rises from within us when we place ourselves in balance with its energies ... By conceiving of these healing energies ... we can tune into them. What we can conceive we can achieve." I would add that we place ourselves in balance with the Healing Sun not by merely looking inside ourselves but first and foremost by adopting an internal attitude of unconditional love.

My illness, which had affinities to chronic fatigue syndrome (CFIDS), multiple chemical sensitivity (MCS) and fibromyalgia, was precipitated by toxicity and trauma from a series of hepatitis and yellow fever vaccines I received in the spring of 1995. After years of intense suffering and trying one expensive (and mostly ineffective) therapy after another, my turning point came when I realized that if I could somehow reset myself at the genetic level, my thirty or so debilitating symptoms would eventually go away.

To recap, I found myself on this path after reading a disturbing book by Horowitz called *Emerging Viruses.*

Basing his claims on meticulous research, Horowitz demonstrates that vaccines are a principle cause of a variety of autoimmune diseases, including AIDS. He further exposes what is in essence covert biowarfare conducted by the medical establishment against an unsuspecting population in *Healing Codes for the Biological Apocalypse*, where a main theme is the use of sound to heal the physical body by restoring it to genetic integrity.

The specific sounds used to restore genetic integrity derive from the ancient Solfeggio scale. This primordial six-note scale, which was dubiously "lost" by the Roman church during the time of Pope Johannes in the 17th Century, was recently rediscovered by Dr. Joseph Puleo as described in *Healing Codes*. Here it is simply necessary to point out that all three DNA activations of the Regenetics Method employ the Solfeggio scale, which some scholars believe to be the sacred set of six notes employed by the Creator to fashion the world in as many days. Specifically, Potentiation employs the note "Mi," a frequency (528 Hz.) that has been used by cutting-edge molecular biologists to repair genetic defects.

Having discovered Horowitz and Puleo, I was then fortunate enough to stumble on another book that greatly expanded my awareness of the immense scope of human potential: *The Cosmic Serpent: DNA and the Origins of Knowledge*, by French anthropologist Jeremy Narby. *The Cosmic Serpent* is an exploration of DNA from a shamanic perspective that describes how sound can be used to stimulate a genetic self-repair mechanism as detailed in Part I. Intrigued (and desperate) enough to delve into this subject, I learned that the power of sound to activate DNA had recently been documented by the Gariaev group in

Russia. Dr. Gariaev and his brilliant team of geneticists and linguists proved that damaged DNA can be healed without gene splicing or other physical manipulation by merely immersing it in radio and light waves keyed to human language frequencies.

According to Gariaev's research, DNA not only assembles proteins through RNA transcription but also stores and communicates data in a decidedly *linguistic* fashion. His team found that the genetic code in potential DNA follows, for practical purposes, the same foundational rules as human languages. In order to prove this, the syntax, semantics and grammar of language and DNA were compared. It was discovered that potential DNA's alkaline sequences closely mirror linguistic communication rules. This strongly suggests that the many human languages did not appear randomly, as is commonly believed, but reflect our essentially similar genetic structure. Supported by Braden's discovery that the ancient Hebrew name for God is code for DNA, Gariaev's findings offer scientific corroboration that in the beginning was the Word!

Gariaev and his colleagues also studied DNA's uncommon electromagnetic behavior. They concluded that living chromosomes function exactly like holographic biocomputers powered by DNA's own laser radiation. The Gariaev team modulated certain linguistic frequencies onto a laser. With this technology of language-modulated codes translated into radio and light waves, they were not only able to heal damaged chromosomes—they also regrew endocrine glands in animals, stimulated regrowth of new adult teeth in humans, and even successfully altered genetic expression. Amazingly, they obtained results similar to those documented by Dr. Yu Dzang

Kangeng, who was the first to employ torsion energy to map DNA sequences between organisms. Using radio and light waves keyed to human language frequencies to rewrite DNA, as opposed to gene splicing, *Gariaev's team literally transformed frog embryos into healthy salamander embryos in the laboratory.*

In this manner metamorphosis was achieved without any of the side effects encountered when manipulating isolated genes. The "random and risky nature of gene splicing has been sadly hidden from the public," warns Horowitz. "With gene therapy, researchers cannot definitively predict where on a [chromosome] the modified gene might land, raising a hazardous possibility of inadvertently disrupting other genetic expressions and cellular functions." Compare this to the organic alteration of genetic expression that can be achieved by simply applying vibration and language (or sound and intention, or *words*) to DNA. Gariaev's historical experiment in embryogenesis points to the immense power of what many are calling wave-genetics, an area which, contrary to current molecular biology dogma and propaganda, has an obviously more primary influence on the origin of species than biochemistry.

Masters such as Jesus and the Buddha have always insisted that our genetic code can be "potentiated" through language—thus the healing effects of prayer, hypnosis, affirmations, mantras, etc. Happily, Gariaev's research has now scientifically substantiated such phenomena. The more developed the individual healer's consciousness, the less need there is for a mechanical crutch.

Human consciousness, not technology, is the key to true enlightenment. Reliance on something outside ourselves such as a technological device to heal us, or make us "whole," is at best giving away our power, at worst worshiping a false god. J. J. Hurtak emphatically argues this point in *The Keys of Enoch*, stating that technology "must not be offered up as our consolation, for ... it would be our desolation. [We] must clearly see the spiritual dialectic taking place between those who choose ... Light as the touchstone for evolution ... [and] those who choose [technology's] codes for containment of the flesh, retrogressive evolution within three-dimensional form, and the annihilation of the hope for spiritual liberation."[16]

Astonishingly, Gariaev's research reveals even more far-reaching implications with respect to the unlimited healing power of human genetic consciousness. The Russian team found that wave-activated DNA can manipulate the space matrix, producing small electromagnetic wormholes of a subquantum nature as

---

[16] In a similar vein, the Weinholds have written of what they call the Path of Technology (as opposed to the Path of Nature), "We have nothing against technology per se, and believe that some devices are helpful as 'boosters.' When created by minds connected to heart and spirit, technology can become a useful, but not essential, spiritual tool for enhancing genuinely spiritual living. Technology lacking connection with heart and spirit becomes just another box from which it is necessary, at some point, to break free." When technology transforms into a path, "it encourages dependency because it implies that people need to rely on a technical intermediary to help them open their own gates of perception. Rather than using primordial tools grounded in nature to empower initiates on their return to Source, the Path of Technology can end up disempowering people and encouraging spiritual co-dependency."

covered in Part I. These DNA-activated wormholes, whose energy signatures are similar to those of Einstein-Rosen bridges found near black holes, are connections between different areas in the multiverse through which data can be transmitted outside space-time.

Potential DNA, which regulates transdimensional self-organization (epigenetic) functions, magnetizes these nonlocal streams of information to itself and then forwards them to our consciousness. Grazyna Fosar and Franz Bludorf, authors of an excellent summary of Gariaev's findings entitled *Vernetzte Intelligenz* ("Networked Intelligence"), refer to this data transfer process as *hypercommunication,* pointing out that it is often experienced as "intuition" or "inspiration."

Remote DNA activation is easily explained as an energenetic transfer of consciousness manifesting as torsion waves that stimulate a molecular rearrangement of transposons in potential DNA. In turn, potential DNA shifts the bioenergy fields, which then modify metabolic and replication functions in cells, facilitating healing. The same process that encourages healing, by inviting more torsion light into cells, by definition promotes enlightenment.

When hypercommunication occurs, according to Fosar and Bludorf, an extraordinary phenomenon can be observed in DNA. They relate how Gariaev irradiated a DNA sample with a laser until a typical wave pattern formed on his monitor. When the DNA sample was extracted, its electromagnetic pattern remained, perfectly intact. Many control experiments established that the pattern still emanated from the absent sample, whose energy field apparently remained undisturbed in the holding chamber for up to thirty days, causing light to spiral all by itself following the shape of the physically removed double helix.

This nonlocal, light-bending torsion energy phenomenon has since become famous as the "DNA phantom effect." It is theorized that torsion waves from outside space and time continue to flow through the activated wormholes even after the DNA is removed. Remote (i.e., distance) DNA activation is thus easily explained as an ener-genetic transfer of consciousness manifesting as torsion waves that stimulate a molecular rearrangement of transposons in potential DNA. In turn, potential DNA shifts the bioenergy fields, which then modify metabolic and replication functions in cells, facilitating healing (Figure 2). This same process of DNA activation that encourages healing, by inviting more torsion light into cells, by definition promotes *enlightenment.*

"Most people tend to think that the DNA created the [phantom] energy field, and that the energy field is somehow just a 'shadow' of the DNA," writes Wilcock, who proposes a fascinating reinterpretation: "However, I believe that the wave actually exists before the DNA ... [The] only logical explanation is that the phantom energy of DNA is actually the *creator* of DNA." Since this phantom spiritual energy pervades the galaxy, wherever the "materials that create life exist, the subtle, spiraling pressure currents of this energy will arrange the DNA molecule into existence."

Combined with much research of my own, my intuition led me to theorize that the correct combination of sounds, intentionally geared to the body's electromagnetics, could invite an influx of torsion energy capable, for instance, of clearing vaccination toxicity and trauma at the genetic level and upgrading the human bioenergy field to higher harmonic functioning. I came to view the electromagnetic fields as an individual's energetic—as well as multidimensional—blueprint that not only can be reset like a blown fuse but, in the process, literally transformed. Leigh and I named this approach to DNA activation the Regenetics Method after Potentiation Electromagnetic Repatterning resolved my chronic illness and we began to develop Articulation and Elucidation. The "fringe benefit" of Potentiation was that it also promoted enlightenment by initiating the first phase of lightbody activation.

13
Historical & Scientific Overview of Enlightenment

Many ancient traditions worldwide maintain that humans not only inherently possess the potential for fully incarnating light at the physiological level, but that some have already achieved it, and millions more will do so in the very era in which we live. The historical literature "suggests that there are unusual physical, as well as psychological, consequences in humans to the attainment of the exalted state of mind known as enlightenment," writes biochemist Colm Kelleher. "These reported changes include, but are not limited to, sudden reversal of aging, emergence of a light body and observed bodily ascension." While many of these descriptions associate the lightbody with death, Kelleher makes it clear that a number of reports indicate that "transformation of the body can happen independently of death."

The path of physical transcendence or bio-spiritual enlightenment through lightbody activation was embraced as a reality in most of the ancient world. The death and resurrection of Christ and Osirus are two famous examples from the Near East. In the Middle Ages, a group known as the Cathars from southern France claimed to possess the secret gospel of Jesus called the Gospel of Love, believed to contain linguistic keys for creating the lightbody. After the existence of this text became known, the Roman church began to torture the Cathars in one of its infamous Inquisitions—at which point the Gospel of Love mysteriously disappeared like the Solfeggio scale.[17]

It seems that the Gospel of Love was, among other things, a manual for creating the merkabah. The merkabah, according to William Henry, is the "light body vehicle of resurrection and ascension that is the foundation of Hebrew mysticism. These texts make it clear that the Mer-Ka-Ba is a vehicle of light that emerges from within the human body." Henry points to the Resurrection, following which the doubting fingers of Thomas appear to enter Christ's transfigured, luminescent flesh, as one famous description of the completely activated lightbody. In the previously cited article entitled "Finding the Holy Grail," which was partly inspired by the Regenetics Method, Barry and Janae Weinhold make a similar claim, pointing out on the basis of decades of in-depth historical research that the "individual human body *is* the Holy Grail. It isn't something 'out there.' Like a tuning fork, the body can be tuned to different frequencies," including that of Source, through DNA activation.

"Many indigenous traditions of Mesoamerica believe that [Source] emits a frequency or tone known as 'Ge' that not only heals the body-mind-spirit but provides immortality," write the Weinholds, adding that the

---

[17] Ironically, owing to the stringent proof requirements for canonization of saints, the Catholic church maintains some of the most detailed records of paranormal phenomena associated with the lightbody, including several instances of individuals levitating, flying, or bilocating.

spiritual practices used in the ancient mystery schools of Egypt and Greece employed a variety of ... vibrational tools to attune people's DNA to Source. This caused the DNA to ring, sing or vibrate so that it resonated with the tone of *Ge*—the frequency of Galactic Center. This attunement activated a *San Graal* or Song Grail—a "love song in the blood"—creating a rainbow bridge that synchronized an initiate's consciousness with Source. This love song energetically united Heaven (Galactic Center) with Earth (initiates), opening human hearts and pumping crystallized Ge-tuned blood through their bodies. From this perspective, "Ge-sus" is a Master Being sent from Tula or Galactic Center to help humanity attune its DNA to the frequency of Ge so that we can return to Source.

In a nearly identical vein, Horowitz writes that "DNA seems to be transmitting the equivalent of heavenly love songs. From this music, played through genetic equipment, variations in sacred geometric forms materialize in space."

The ankh or key of life is of a musical nature and designed to be employed along with a type of inspired (and inspiring) speech known as the **Language of the Birds**. *This powerful combination, properly performed, keys potential DNA to build the Holy Grail or lightbody.*

The profound and numerous connections between the Egyptian Osirus and Jesus have been noted by generations of scholars. Among many other similarities, both are linked to the phoenix or heron, represented in hieroglyphics coming from Galactic Center, also (as indicated in the above quote by the Weinholds) called

Tula, carrying the key of life. In Egyptian hieroglyphics this key appears as an ankh, which may have been a type of actual tuning fork for harmonizing with Galactic Center, or may have merely symbolized techniques (such as use of the Solfeggio scale) for producing this celestial harmonization. In either case, the ankh or key of life is of a musical nature and designed to be employed along with a type of inspired (and inspiring) speech known as the *Language of the Birds*. This powerful combination, properly performed, keys potential DNA to build the Holy Grail or lightbody.

The Language of the Birds, according to the Weinholds who cite Henry's research, "is a vowel-only phonetic code ... Genetic and linguistic research indicates that the five vowels correspond to the five letters used to represent DNA and RNA ... Initiates of the Language of the Birds who are able to speak or tone these vowels in certain ways know that these sounds permanently activate the DNA of all those who are able and willing to hear."

At the genetic level, such a radical activation, according to Kelleher's previously discussed research in transposons, occurs through a *transposition burst* involving the molecular rearrangement of perhaps thousands of genes. Consistent with Braden's hypothesis regarding dormant DNA activation as well as Wilcock's compelling model of spontaneous evolution that simultaneously transmutes both consciousness and biology, Kelleher insists that true enlightenment, in addition to being a mental state, appears to have *physical* consequences.

The "appearance of a light body as a result of attaining enlightenment ... could be described as the emergence of a new species in a single generation from humanity," he writes, adding that a "synchronized, non random transposition burst is the most simple molecular mechanism to account for the required new configuration." While pointing out based on the historical literature that lightbody creation appears to occur only "in humans who have attained spiritual mastery," Kelleher emphasizes the existence of "stages on the road to ... enlightenment [that are] experienced by a great number of ordinary people." This supports the potential effectiveness of a step-by-step process, such as the Regenetics Method, to bio-spiritual enlightenment in which transposons are incrementally stimulated in preparatory phases—culminating in a "synchronized, non random transposition burst" when, and only when, the individual is consciously prepared to experience it.

In one apocryphal text known as the *Pistis Sophia*, Jesus (considered a master of the Language of the Birds) discourses on the afterlife in terms that appear straight out of the Egyptian *Book of the Dead*. Henry calls this "the first lesson of the Mer-Ka-Ba mysticism." "You are to seek after the mysteries of the Light," Jesus is quoted as saying, "which purify the body and make it into refined light." Later, Jesus describes the connection between our dimension and higher dimensions as operating "from within outwards"—a statement, according to Henry, that "refers to a transformation of consciousness that opens the door to other worlds." Similarly, in the Bible Jesus insists, *The Kingdom of Heaven is within*. Horowitz's research leads him to affirm the material truth of this assertion: "The bioacoustic and electromagnetic matrix through which the Holy Spirit flows is real. It's what animates your DNA [by transmitting] the Kingdom of

Heaven to you, and through you, right now, on Earth as it is in Heaven."

Another important figure from the Mediterranean associated with the lightbody or soul body is the Egyptian Thoth, called Hermes Trimegistus by the Greeks and considered the father of alchemy. Thoth is credited with the enormously influential phrase "As above, so below." Of the many seemingly miraculous gifts he brought his people, arguably Thoth's most important legacy is the doctrine of inner or spiritual light that can literally metamorphose the human body into a physiology of divine radiance. Interestingly, Thoth was also revered as the creator of writing and his alchemical science of transformation, like that of Jesus, is associated with the Language of the Birds.

The lightbody is also a theme in the ancient mystical traditions of Central and South America. A variety of mythical figures exist similar to the Incan god-man Amanumuru, who according to legend walked through a portal called the Muru Doorway and returned via the Black Road to his true home among the stars. In what is today Mexico, a figure known as Quetzalcoatl embodied the higher light of divinity. Judith Polich has called Quetzalcoatl "the Osirus of Mesoamerica" and sees him as symbolizing the bridging of duality, a being who "represents light in physical form ... freed from the confines of matter."

It seems poetic justice that Quetzalcoatl is usually depicted as a serpent with bird wings—an obvious reference to the ability of DNA (symbolized by the serpent) to transform one into an angelic being capable of *f/light*, which is an excellent definition of the merkabah. Equally important is that Quetzalcoatl is thought to have revitalized the great ceremonial center of Teotihuacán, believed by some archeologists to be Earth's interdimensional gateway to the legendary Tula, the celestial home of Quetzalcoatl—and perhaps other "messianic" herons or phoenixes who arrived in this dimension carrying the key of life, or the knowledge of how to inspire ("breathe life") by speaking or singing the bio-spiritual Language of the Birds.

Elucidation Triune Activation, the third and final DNA activation in the Regenetics Method, is designed to establish the ener-genetic precondition for lightbody expression. This is done by employing the Solfeggio scale in tandem with the Language of the Birds to activate the brain's triune cortex, sometimes called (curiously enough) the "bird brain" as opposed to the mammalian and reptilian cortices beneath it. The human brain can be compared to a three-stop roadmap that unambiguously charts the spontaneous evolutions of our species from reptilian to mammalian and now to "angelic." Not surprisingly, this final cortex that is currently activating in many people has been scientifically demonstrated to be the only light-sensitive layer of our three-part brain—capable of tracking the movement of the sun, for instance, even from inside a windowless room.

Here it must be stressed that much of the information mainstream science has propagated about biology is misinformation and perhaps disinformation: certainly incorrect and perhaps intentionally misleading. For example, in humans the brain and central nervous system are not composed entirely of organic matter; they also contain up to ten percent of the following six precious metals: gold, iridium, osmium, palladium, platinum, and rhodium.[18] This fact has remained largely hidden from the public at least in part because current technology is simply not designed to detect such metals that normally exist in human physiology in multidimensional states. Kinesiological testing reveals these six metals energetically correspond to, and can be activated by, the six notes of the Solfeggio scale.

Combined with a specific vowel-only phonetic code that medieval alchemists referred to as the Green Language and I have been calling the Language of the Birds, the six notes of the Solfeggio scale can be voiced, as they are in Elucidation, to activate the six precious metals that form part of the triune cortex.

Renowned historian Sir Laurence Gardner, bestselling author of *Bloodline of the Holy Grail* and *Genesis of the Grail Kings,* offers evidence that these six extraordinary metals that form part of the triune cortex and central nervous system not only exist in humans but can be made to align their atomic spins so as to become higher-dimensional and thereby create an internal source of torsion energy that manifests as light. Certain "areas of the brain can be stimulated to extend human consciousness beyond any imagining," writes Gardner when discussing the prized alchemical knowledge contained in the *Book of Thoth.* By activating our internal "chassis" of precious metals, we can stimulate creation of the lightbody from within. This internal energy is often

---

[18] This special family of metals should not be confused with environmental non-monatomic heavy metals such as mercury and lead which are highly toxic to human cells.

called kundalini, which according to Vedic teachings, has the potential to unfold one's complete bio-spiritual enlightenment (the lightbody) when fully awakened.

Combined with a specific vowel-only phonetic code that medieval alchemists referred to as the Green Language and I have been calling the Language of the Birds, the six notes of the Solfeggio scale can be voiced, as they are in Elucidation, to activate the six precious metals that form part of the triune cortex. This initiates a progressive monatomic "high-spin" effect that produces bioacoustic and bioelectric signals capable of turning the body's liquid crystals from hexagons into interlocking tetrahedrons or merkabahs (Figure 7). This phenomenon is somewhat akin to the use of kind words to metamorphose the shape of water molecules as documented in recent Japanese studies conducted by Masaru Emoto. Dr. Emoto's fascinating research establishes that torsion or subspace energy generated by human language can alter the structure of water. When the water in question surrounds the DNA molecule—and all DNA in the body is surrounded by water—it has the vibratory power to transfer its new molecular structure to the genome via transposons.

In the case of tetrahedral water molecules (whose tripartite form recalls the trinity), this highly structured and energized liquid compound penetrates the membrane of cells, harmonically signaling potential DNA to begin creating the lightbody. Potential DNA, in turn, projects a new unified frequency or "consciousness field" around the body. The ener-genetic precondition for lightbody expression, the Unified Consciousness Field is no longer composed of energy gradations in the form of electromagnetic bands but is truly a gestalt that gradually comes to resonate throughout at Source's signature tone of *Ge*—at which point the individual consciousness grounding itself in the lightbody can be considered fully unified with Source, or enlightened.

I propose the paradox that the "tone" of Ge is not really a frequency as we understand the term but rather absolute *Silence*, the omnipotent creational *Stillness* of unconditional love that differentiates into torsion waves of sound and then light during the threefold process of universal manifestation. The void state, Silent Stillness, is the primal formative matrix and "proportionately our most fundamental reality," Iona Miller and Richard Miller remind us in "From Helix to Hologram." "In essence, we emerge from pre-geometrically structured nothingness. DNA is the projector" of our reality from the embryonic stage forward.

In another article recently published in *DNA Monthly* entitled "The Universe Is Obsolete: A Gallery of Multiverse Theories," Iona Miller and Richard Miller theorize on Silent Stillness from a more cosmological perspective. "Sound waves originated in the first instant of the universe's life," they propose. "Vacuum-spawned particles flickering into existence from the Void were energized ... to remain in the real world. This sudden influx of countless particles from the vacuum was like throwing a stone into the dense particle pond of the early universe. Pressure waves rippling through the gas were nothing more than sound waves. The entire universe rang like a bell." The authors go on to postulate that the particle fog then "cleared and the universe became transparent. There was no longer enough pressure to support the sound waves. But now photons traveled freely through space ('Let there be Light')."

Another article reprinted in *DNA Monthly* further addresses the relationship between sound and light. In "Music to the Ears: The Infrared Frequencies of DNA Bases," composer Susan Alexjander relates how, with the assistance of renowned biologist David Deamer, she was able to measure the infrared energies of DNA nucleotides, translate them into sound, and thereby create an unprecedented type of DNA music. Alexjander explains,

> An octave in light is the same ratio as an octave in sound—2:1. A perfect fifth, or a relationship of 3:2, is the same proportion in light as in sound and can be interpolated to the world of geometry, architecture, movements of the planets, and so forth, so long as there is a periodic or regular vibration. By discovering patterns of ratios in light, we are simply translating into a sound medium to "hear" information and assess interrelationships. It could also be argued that both light and sound refer back to a common archetype which, as yet, is unknown to us, not unlike cousins who relate back to a common relative.

This archetypal "common relative" of light and sound, I contend, is Silent Stillness.

The divine triune structure of Silent Stillness giving rise to Sound (the Word or Holy Spirit) which then becomes Light (the sun or Son) is one way of conceptualizing the Sacred Trinity (Figure 8). When this trinitized energy has finally expressed itself in and as the Unified Consciousness Field, our cells can begin to replicate a new tetrahedral crystallinity, a biological trinity, based on the Adam Kadmon or lightbody template. This is a deeply personal and internal process that, in the end, requires the individual to adapt his or her own belief

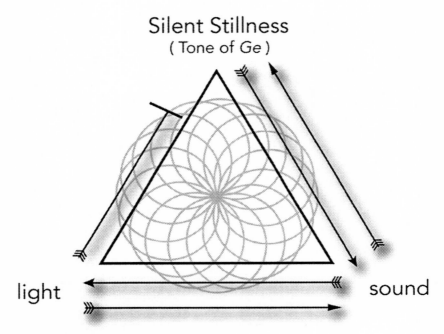

Figure 8: The Sacred Trinity
The image above illustrates the threefold process of universal manifestation in which Silent Stillness (the "tone" of *Ge*) gives rise to sound, which then translates into light (the holographic multiverse). Note that to return "home" to Source, we must retrace our steps from light to sound. Attempting to achieve bio-spiritual enlightenment without embracing the Audible Life Stream is a short-cut that leads to a dead-end.

system (the spiritual subtle body) to accept enlightenment as a biological reality. Creation of such a biological reality is, I propose, the ultimate form of healing or *wholing*.

The creational trinity composed of nothingness, sound and light is not unique to the Western worldview; it is also foregrounded in many Eastern philosophies. In Taoism, to cite one example, Silent Stillness is referred to as the *Tao*. The Tao gives rise to what Lao Tzu, author of the Tao Te Ching, calls the "ten thousand things" (the light-based holographic multiverse) by way of the breath (sound). From this perspective, Lao Tzu's references to "Immortals" are likely not metaphors but indicate those "sages" who have arrived at bio-spiritual transcendence, or "holy flesh," by activating their lightbodies.

Lightbody creation is a deeply personal and internal process that, in the end, requires the individual to adapt his or her own belief system (the spiritual subtle body) to accept enlightenment as a biological reality. Creation of such a biological reality is, I propose, the ultimate form of healing or wholing.

Polich, calling the divine lightbody blueprint the "god-seed," offers a helpful analogy for how the Adam Kadmon unfolds both individually and collectively: the "seed of any flower has within it a hidden code contained in the plant's DNA that becomes activated under certain conditions ... Similarly, the light codes within the human form may be viewed as spiritual DNA ... the inner forces that trigger the process of enlightenment. The ultimate maturation of the god-seed ... is divinity, an example of which is Christ consciousness."

On a species level, accessing Christ or unity consciousness implies being capable of naturally utilizing hypercommunication. In the animal kingdom, hypercommunication has been successfully employed for millions of years. Fosar and Bludorf point to the minutely orchestrated flow of life in insect colonies as an example. When a queen ant is separated from her colony, construction normally continues. If the queen is killed, however, all work stops. Apparently, the queen sends the "construction blueprint" even from great distances via the collective consciousness/DNA of her colony. She can be as far away as she wants, as long as she remains alive.

Fosar and Bludorf compellingly argue that during prehistory humanity was, like most animal species, closely connected to group consciousness. To evolve and experience individuality, and ultimately individuation, humans chose to abandon hypercommunication almost completely. Now that we are relatively grounded in our individual consciousness, we are in a position to create a new network of group consciousness: one in which we obtain access to all information via our DNA—a conclusion with many similarities to Sheldrake's concept of Morphic Resonance. Just as with the Internet, Fosar and Bludorf demonstrate, *one can "upload" data into the biological Internet that is DNA, "download" data from it, and even "email" other participants.*

It is my personal belief, one I share with Leigh and perhaps millions of others, that the time is quickly approaching for the maturation of the god-seed and global lightbody activation leading to a hypercommunication revolution with the ability to unite all of humanity as a differentiated, enlightened consciousness. "The age that has been written about, whispered about, and spoken about is upon you," writes Marciniak. "It is the age when humanity physically mutates ... and literally turns into something ... it was not a short time before ... multidimensional beings." For the ancient Incas, our generation, which is fortunate enough to experience the "end of history" with the Galactic Alignment of 2012, is poised to become the true *chakarunas*, "the bridge people" tasked with creating Heaven on Earth.

14
From Biology to Triology

The evolution from human to divine consciousness involves healing duality and its legacy of karma and disease at the cellular and atomic levels. There is no illness that cannot be healed through the proper exercise of intention. Many of the thousands of documented so-called miracle healings powerfully demonstrate the impact of consciousness on physical as well as emotional, mental and spiritual wellbeing. Mind-body medicine, which is statistically valid enough to be taught in today's medical schools, offers additional proof of our ability to heal ourselves. Bruce Lipton's research further indicates that people can modify their DNA and overcome life-threatening illnesses simply by changing their consciousness.

Deepak Chopra has remarked that "the similarity between a thought and a photon is very deep." A photon is a particle or quantum of light or other electromagnetic radiation. Dr. Chopra is implying a connection between thought and light. To reiterate, in the Regenetics model, *thought (intention) is considered a form or function of torsion energy manifesting as higher-dimensional light.* Mind is "the illuminating energy which 'Lights the way' of an idea or form to be transmitted and received," wrote Alice Bailey. "Upon a beam of light can the energy of the mind materialize." Following this line of reasoning, we can imagine ourselves not only as frozen light (recalling Richard Gerber) but also as "frozen thought."

Looking at the human body as a congealed thought, which may at first strike the reader as strange, is in the final analysis deeply empowering. Quantum physicists have repeatedly demonstrated that a scientist always affects the outcome of an experiment simply by observing it, a realization now universally accepted in the scientific community as the Heisenberg Uncertainty Principle. Even more amazing is the paradigm-altering discovery that gave rise to the aforementioned particle-wave duality: the probability that the physicist actually *creates* the quantum particles he or she observes, since in unobserved states these particles appear to exist only as waves.

A fundamental and revolutionary truth emerges from this information: *consciousness creates.* As human beings imbued with free will, we can use the power of our consciousness to re-create our reality: including but not limited to a body, mind and spirit free of disease.

I emphasize "re-create" because, clearly, we already inhabit one creation. The world as we know it is based on the principle of duality. Another way of stating this is that a dualized or divided consciousness, one that already saw itself as separate from other consciousnesses, including unity or God consciousness, gave birth to the universe as humans typically experience it: a battleground between good and evil, light and dark, right and wrong, "us" and "them."

But duality is not merely a philosophy; it is a physical state of being as well. The very atoms that make up our cells are based on positive and negative charges whose opposition sustains a certain life-form. Lipton has coined the phrase the "biology of consciousness" to summarize the transformational idea that living organisms, including humans, rather than being empirical givens, are actually malleable *thought-forms*. In other words, adopting a quantum perspective, we are basically waves that only cohere as particles through an act of consciousness. By changing our consciousness, we change our physical form and functioning.

> *Lipton has coined the phrase the "biology of consciousness" to summarize the transformational idea that living organisms, including humans, rather than being empirical givens, are actually malleable* thought-forms. *In other words, adopting a quantum perspective, we are basically waves that only cohere as particles through an act of consciousness. By changing our consciousness, we change our physical form and functioning.*

Healing, as previously pointed out, means to make whole. Healing results in unification or enlightenment and implies atonement, which in this context should be read as "at-one-ment."[19] In a world where thought creates and biology is a product of consciousness, not the other way around, the mind has the power to forge a new biology, one no longer based on duality but on principles of unity and harmony. In *Return of the Bird Tribes*, where

---

[19] According to Horowitz, *atonement* "has at least three important meanings: 1) 'at-one-ment,' or becoming *one* with the Creator; 2) 'a-tone-meant,' or an *intended* sound, electromagnetic frequency, or mathematical vibration [and] 3) 'a-tone-meant,' or the *meaning* of a tone reflecting the meaning of life as a creative concert of life-sustaining ... sound, electromagnetic frequencies, and bioacoustic resonances interacting with matter."

145

a central theme is the reunion of the human body with the soul in the pivotal years we are currently experiencing, Ken Carey neatly summarizes how we must proceed, individually as well as collectively: "In the order of healing, it is human consciousness that first must change." Our challenge, which is also a tremendous opportunity, is to open up to a literally life-changing way of thinking ourselves into existence.

Enlightenment, as elaborated in previous chapters, is the process of raising consciousness and letting the light of soul in to the point that we *become* it. True enlightenment follows a path of conscious personal mastery that results in transformation and, by definition, involves creation of a stable lightbody. The lightbody or soul body is a trinitized (balanced and harmonious) physical vehicle that has resolved duality, karma and disease at the cellular and atomic levels.

We can conceptualize the current evolutionary Shift in our species' DNA as a change in operating systems from a binary to a "trinary" code based on the energenetics of the threefold tetrahedron shape. We might even go so far as to say that humans are evolving out of biology into "triology."

We can conceptualize the current evolutionary Shift in our species' DNA as a change in operating systems from a binary to a "trinary" code based on the energenetics of the threefold tetrahedron shape. We might even go so far as to say that humans are evolving out of biology into "triology." In this light it is most interesting to recall that some members of the alternative science community have alluded to suppressed research on a third

DNA strand reportedly activating in many humans (Figure 6).

An illuminating way of visualizing how metamorphosis into a unified light-based physiology occurs is to look at a quantum particle known as positronium. Positronium is composed of an electron, which has a negative charge, and a positron, which has a positive charge. Positronium is a perfect example of duality. It also provides a wonderful illustration of how the lightbody is created. Since electrons and positrons are antiparticle opposites, after combining to form positronium, they immediately cancel out each other and decay into two particles or quanta of light (photons). A third stable and unified element, which is neither positive nor negative, is thus created from a preexisting dualism.

Barbara Hand Clow writes that this process of combination and decay in the positronium atom, mirrored in lightbody activation, "resolves inherent duality into light ... [As] the electron is the basic unit of activation—life—it triggers the transmutation of the positron—karma." Contrary to popular misconception, karma has nothing to do with punishment and reward. It exists as part of our holographic universe's binary or dualistic operating system only to teach us responsibility for our creations—and *all* things we experience are our creations. When these creations are out of tune with Source, they often manifest in the disharmony known as disease. This can occur not only in individuals but in entire civilizations. In both cases, disease, which is typically considered a crisis, simultaneously serves as a powerful stimulus for transformation and transcendence.

As we raise our consciousness and activate our lightbody, we realize we are our own creators made, or making ourselves, in the image and similitude of the one Creator. Indeed, since in a hologram the part contains the whole, we *are* the one Creator. By learning this truly transformative lesson, we return to unity consciousness while mastering physicality. In other words, we achieve god-realization as the light of soul descends into a divine or soul body healed of duality and freed from the instructional cycle of karma. This process of resolving duality and its legacy requires healing the Fragmentary Body, which can be initiated with a specific genetic activation and bioenergy recalibration like that accomplished through Potentiation Electromagnetic Repatterning.

If consciousness creates, and reality including biology is a thought-form, and in the beginning was indeed the Word, then it is critical we realize that a divided consciousness employing some type of divisive *sound* combined with a separatist *intention* gave birth to our dualistic universe. The notion that we are children of a lesser god (or lesser aspect of ourselves) goes back at least as far as the Gnostics, whose humane yet cosmic philosophy profoundly inspired Jesus. To summarize, the Gnostics believed that the universe and its inhabitants are imperfect (i.e., unhealed) manifestations arising from a false sense of separation from Source—the Original Wound—and that the ultimate goal of life on Earth is to return to a state of enlightenment or wholeness.

Citing a line from William Blake, "God is man and exists in us and we in him," Braden in *The God Code* exhibits a philosophy very much in line with Gnostic thought when he reiterates, "God exists as humankind so that humankind may make the choices each day that bring us closer to the perfection of our Creator." Elsewhere, Braden's Gnostic orientation appears even more pronounced. "The Book of Genesis provides some of the most powerful clues to understanding our role in the destiny of our species," he writes. "In its original language of Hebrew, the text reveals that during the act of creation, God stopped the process *before* it was complete (Genesis 17:1). The English translation of this telling event reads: 'I am God the Creator who said enough, now walk before me and *become* perfect.'"

Clow displays a similar "Gnostic" cosmology when writing about what has been called "the Fall": "You walked out of the Garden of Eden ... and ... split your world by viewing it through your eyes and brain instead of feeling it in your heart. The greenness of your world became separate from you, and time began." Clow also associates the Fall with speech. After humanity attempted to name the Creator, she writes, "then everything had to have a name; *language began as an identification process instead of using sound as a resonation tool ... for perceptual fusion*" such as that characteristic of a system of hypercommunication.

From a somewhat more scholarly angle, Charles Eisenstein in *The Ascent of Humanity* argues essentially the same point. "The ascent of humanity is in part a descent into a language of conventional symbols, representations of reality instead of the integrated vocal dimension," he explains. "This gradual distancing, in which and through which language assumed a mediatory function, paralleled, contributed to, and resulted from the generalized separation of man and nature. It is the discrete and separate self that desires to name the things of nature, or that could even conceive of doing so." Specifying that to name "is to dominate, to categorize, to subjugate and, quite literally, to objectify," Eisenstein concludes, "No wonder in Genesis, Adam's first act in confirmation of his God-given dominion over the animals is to name them."

Similarly, in *Healing Sounds* Jonathan Goldman relates,

> There are legends that before there was a spoken language of words, there was a harmonic language. This language allowed humankind to communicate with all the creations of nature [utilizing] the concept of information ... encoded on ... pure tone frequencies ... This may be one of the ways ... dolphins communicate [by] transmitting three-dimensional holographic thought-forms of sound. Eventually this harmonic language separated [when] consonants combined with the tones to create words.

These legends, like the basic cosmology behind nearly all religions and mythologies, prioritize the creational energy of sound combined with intention. Together, these form a divine language of creation called by alchemists the Green Language and known in the Koran as the Language of the Birds. To paraphrase another of Goldman's equations, vocalization + visualization = manifestation, we can affirm that SOUND + INTENTION = CREATION.

From our previous discussion of the literal alphabet that is DNA, it should be obvious that science is beginning to confirm this belief in the life-giving primordial Word (a generative electromagnetic and bioacoustic interface consciously imbued with meaning) that provides the foundation for the overwhelming majority of the world's spiritual belief systems.

When discussing Regenetics, Leigh and I regularly refer to sound and intention. From the time we began developing our method, we intuitively felt that of these two energies, sound is primary. Only later did we come to understand that sound derives directly from the unified torsion energy of unconditional love, the Silent Stillness sometimes reached in meditation. The idea that light stems from sound may strike some readers as contrary to what is observed in nature, where sound operates at a measurably lower vibratory rate than light. Here, however, we are discussing sound and light *in higher-dimensional states* where other laws of physics apply. Arguably, *opposite* laws—rather, the same laws running in reverse order—apply, given the cosmic mirroring inherent in the concept of "As above, so below."

Richard Miller and Iona Miller are two of a growing number of researchers who believe that the creational energy emanating from Galactic Center (the "tone" of Ge) begins as sound and manifests as light that creates the holographic illusion of reality—a translation process detailed in Chapter Six that is precisely replicated in the human body at the level of chromosomes. The thirteenth-century Persian saint Shamas-i-Tabriz shared a similar belief, eloquently proposing that

> The Universe was manifested out of
> The Divine Sound;
> From It came into being the Light.

Perfectly consistent with this line of reasoning, the residual energy of the so-called Big Bang, at first dismissed as "background noise," was picked up by *radio telescopes*.[20]

Some scholars, such as Henry and the Weinholds (as noted), go so far as to argue that the famous quest for the Holy Grail is actually a quest to attune our DNA so that it resonates with Galactic Center's tone of Ge. This divine "frequency" capable of generating a "love song in the blood," a *San Graal* (Holy Blood) or "Song Grail," can in turn attune the core of our being, our DNA, to the galactic Core's transformational "vibration" of unconditional love. To transcend our multidimensional existence based in light and reunite with our transdimensional Source in the Silent Stillness that gives rise to sound, then, appears to be the ultimate goal of the true spiritual seeker. That we do this in a vehicle called the lightbody poetically confirms that we travel the path of light until we encounter the Word.

"The point comes in the life of every sincere spiritual seeker," writes Dennis Holtje in a fascinating

---

[20] The cosmological model of creation I am proposing in which sound gives rise to light is not only consistent with the majority of world religions and mythologies and the genetic sound-light translation mechanism. This model may also help bridge the gap currently dividing those physicists invested in dark matter and those who follow the Electric Universe theory. The latter contend that the existence of plasma as an operative principle in cosmology does away with the necessity for looking to other dimensions for missing matter. If, however, we consider plasma "liquefied light," the form light takes during manifestation, both theories may be essentially correct. Since matter and energy are interchangeable, we can imagine a continuous movement of matter or torsion energy in the form of higher-dimensional light into our own dimension, where it manifests as plasma before becoming "physical."

book entitled *From Light to Sound: The Spiritual Progression,* "when information, knowledge, and finespun theory no longer satisfy our innate quest for spiritual liberation ... Should we desire a more fulfilling ... relationship with soul and the God within, we must surpass the reach of this light energy and experience the spiritual energy which parents it—the Sound Current." In other words, light is about information whereas sound is about *transformation.* We can spend lifetimes following the light trying one spiritual and/or intellectual technique after another, but until we embrace what Holtje elsewhere calls the Audible Life Stream, we will never find our way home.

> **Light is about information whereas sound is about transformation. *We can spend lifetimes following the light trying one spiritual and/or intellectual technique after another, but until we embrace the Audible Life Stream, we will never find our way home.***

The point I am making is that although it can be discussed, enlightenment is not a cerebral process and cannot be reasoned out; it must be *experienced* at the creational level of sound. "The stunning simplicity of the Sound energy confounds the mind," explains Holtje. "We are conditioned to use the mind to solve all of life's dilemmas, unaware that the latent energy of Sound, once released, provides the permanent solution of awakened spiritual living." With sound, writes Marciniak on a related note, "it is quite easy to bypass the logical mind." Moreover, the evolution of "DNA expresses itself beyond logic through sound."

Clow seems to posit something resembling the aforementioned transdimensional home in her vision of a "perceptually fused" reality generated through hypercommunication that predated objectifying human language and our species' Fall from grace (unity). While admitting that "biology must merge with love" if humans are to evolve their "triology of consciousness," she elsewhere implies that the infinite creational energy of Source is ultimately unknowable.

This view is out of sync with the notion of god-seed and -realization that sees the current stage of human evolution as a process of meeting our Maker while still very much alive. The fundamental reality we are now being called to embody is that we are one with the Maker. Indeed, we *are* our Maker.

Such unified perception results from transcending duality, which is accomplished through opening our hearts to unconditional love and evolving into unity consciousness and its corresponding physiology of light— an epistemological and ontological enlightenment that at some point necessarily involves healing the *perception* of duality. In turn, healing the perception of duality allows us to resolve duality in our spiritual, emotional, mental and physical bodies by incarnating the soul (whose "sole" principle is unity) in the form of the lightbody.

15
"So Below, As Above"

Given that the very atoms that comprise matter are dualized into positive and negative, it should come as no surprise that duality also expresses itself in the body's electromagnetic fields. This brings us back to the critically important but largely overlooked concept of the Fragmentary Body occasionally encountered in theosophical teachings and introduced in Chapter Seven.

Through muscle testing on hundreds of clients, as related in Part I, Leigh and I found that the second electromagnetic field (which corresponds to the second or sex chakra) exists in most people as a bioenergy or consciousness vacuum that to a significant degree separates spirit and matter. The Fragmentary Body does this by draining one's kundalini (the individual's own life-wave of torsion energy) as it seeks to rise into the higher auric fields and chakras, while impeding the free flow of torsion energy or universal creative consciousness emanating from Galactic Center that seeks to infuse the lower fields and chakras. The Fragmentary Body represents a major impediment to the sacred marriage between the lower self and Higher Self, or the embodiment of the light of soul that occurs during genuine enlightenment.

The Fragmentary Body constitutes an electromagnetic "rift" in the human bioenergy fields that corresponds to the Great Rift dividing the consciousness that created the system of duality, visibly manifest in the night sky as the band of the Milky Way. Such mirroring is entirely in keeping with "As above, so below," since this holographic principle that conflates the part with the whole requires that our consciousness-based physiology be consistent with the cosmological consciousness that created and sustains us.

The Fragmentary Body is not only associated with sexuality but also with the mouth and specifically the tongue: our speech organs. This connection further supports the widespread belief that our dualistic universe was literally spoken or sung into being. The primacy of speech in creation is perhaps why the Egyptian goddess Nu, one of many feminine icons for Galactic Center, is pictured in hieroglyphics as a great milk cow with full *udders*. Today scientists and theologians alike are beginning to agree that if we were indeed created, we were *uttered* into existence.

During the time leading up to the Tower of Babel, which I see as a metaphor for the perceptually fused or unified state of consciousness (hypercommunication) that preceded humanity's experimental and educational Fall from grace that created optimal conditions for individuation, the Bible records that "the whole Earth was of one language, and of one speech." The stories of the Garden of Eden and Tower of Babel are of special interest to our discussion because they directly associate human biology with language. While the language of the Garden is divisive, that of the Tower is both unified and unifying, leading upward (not unlike a vertical DNA helix, the Sacred Spiral) to a heavenly marriage between human and divine.

The divine language of the Tower, spoken by Jesus and called the Language of the Birds, the Green Language and also the *lingua adamica*, is composed exclusively of vowels.[21] This was a major reason the five vowels were extracted from written Hebrew: they were revered as sacrosanct, God's language of creation. "The vowels were 'extras' in Hebrew," writes William Grey in *The Talking Tree*. "The vowels were originally very special sonics indeed, being mostly used for 'God-names' and other sacred purposes. Consonants gave words their bodies, but vowels put soul into them."

Mastery of the Language of the Birds effectively turns one into a master geneticist not only capable of creating life-forms via speech, but of evolving these life-forms into **light-forms** *structured on the tripartite tetrahedron shape that is the basic building block of the merkabah.*

It appears that the five vowels are indeed sacred because, among other things, they correspond to the five nucleotides of DNA and RNA used to create biological organisms: adenine, cytosine, guanine, thymine, and uracil. These five nucleotides, represented as A, C, G, T and U, literally form our genetic alphabet. Mastery of the

---

[21] Medieval alchemists used the phrase the Green Language probably owing to the critical alteration of hydrogen bonds (which are green on the electromagnetic spectrum) in biological water molecules that occurs during lightbody creation. Not surprisingly, many figures associated with the lightbody, such as Osirus and Quetzalcoatl, are typically depicted as green. Similarly, Lao Tzu's Immortals achieve bio-spiritual enlightenment by creating a "jade body."

Language of the Birds effectively turns one into a master geneticist not only capable of creating life-forms via speech, but of evolving these life-forms into *light-forms* structured on the tripartite tetrahedron shape that is the basic building block of the merkabah.

The Fragmentary Body is electromagnetic evidence of misuse or mispronunciation of the Language of the Birds, apparently through insertion of consonants that disrupt the unified flow of vowels and create dualistic syllables. The story of the Garden of Eden appears to record this historical speech event that gave rise to duality in the form of the Fragmentary Body—which energetically corresponds not only to the mouth and tongue but also (appropriately given the procreative "doom" that results from Adam and Eve's fateful discussion of knowledge) the genitals.

The Fragmentary Body is electromagnetic evidence of misuse or mispronunciation of the Language of the Birds, apparently through insertion of consonants that break up the unified flow of vowels and create dualistic syllables.

With many parallels to Eckhart Tolle's concept of the "pain body" that keeps people from accessing the infinite "Power of Now," the Fragmentary Body operates much like a deep scratch in a record or, to use a Vedic term, a *samskara* that maintains one's consciousness locked in a limited (unenlightened) matrix of thought and belief banished from knowledge or gnosis of unity with the Garden or Ground of Being. Toltec masters often refer to the Fragmentary Body as the Parasite—fittingly, since at the energetic level, parasites (physical and aetheric) enter and establish themselves at the human organism's expense by way of the Fragmentary Body. In all cases, the Fragmentary Body is a dualistic principle of limitation that promotes disconnection from Source and, ultimately, death.

While developing Potentiation Electromagnetic Repatterning, Leigh and I became increasingly interested in this problematic second auric field. We were also intrigued by the fact that, using muscle testing, we were consistently finding nine electromagnetic fields corresponding to nine chakras. Our understanding from theosophy and Vedic teachings was that there were only seven fields and seven chakras. But thousands of kinesiological tests convinced us there are nine fields and nine chakras, in addition to a tenth energy center associated with Galactic Center.

We concluded that this tenth field (which generates the unifying tone of Ge) is where the Higher or God Self, also known as the soul or atmic permanent atom, resides. While the other four permanent atoms (physical, emotional, mental, and spiritual) are associated in dualistic pairs with particular lower electromagnetic fields as indicated in Appendix C, the atmic remains unified in the Master or Source Field. It thus represents the divine or soul aspect of ourselves that never experiences fragmentation and loss of unity consciousness through duality. In other words, the atmic permanent atom, or Adam, was never banished from the Garden. This is also the part of ourselves that is now seeking to transmute our consciousness and biology—via the *lingua adamica*, no less—so that we can evolve into what we have always been *in potentia*: the Adam Kadmon.

What happened next in our process of ener-genetic unfoldment was extremely exciting. After Leigh and I performed Potentiation on ourselves and began to experience what we came to understand as torsion energy from Galactic Center activating our DNA, we realized that two significant shifts, both of which we substantiated through kinesiology, were happening in our energy bodies.

First, the vibratory frequency of our electromagnetic fields began noticeably increasing. Second and more importantly, the fields themselves were undergoing a progressive recalibration from nine to eight in number. In this process, the ninth field literally descended and sealed the second field or Fragmentary Body, allowing the spiritual energy of the Healing Sun to flow through our electromagnetic fields and chakras uninterrupted for the first time. It was at this point that my health began to improve dramatically and Leigh's asthma and environmental allergies completely disappeared.

In retrospect, this energetic repatterning makes perfect sense. By bridging the rift in our bioenergy fields created by the Fragmentary Body, we were taking a first step toward healing duality at the level of our biology. We were also electromagnetically recalibrating to eight energy centers, which represents a critical alchemical phase of lightbody activation having to do with creating an infinity circuit in the electromagnetic blueprint. The number 8 has always been of utmost importance to masters of the Language of the Birds. Thoth was known as the Lord of 8, the Buddha taught the Eightfold Path to enlightenment, and numerologically, the name Jeshua (Jesus) translates as 888.

* * *

In her discussion of duality and karma, Clow makes a highly intriguing observation. The centerpiece of her cosmology is the Photon Band, which, to reiterate, can be visualized as a higher-dimensional torsion lattice of light connecting Earth to Galactic Center via the sun that serves as a guiding data communication network for human and planetary evolution (Figure 5).

As we release karma and create our lightbody, Clow writes, our positrons and *"electrons collide, quanta of light are formed, and the Photon Band manifests!"* In other words, we are not merely passive receivers of evolutionary energy; we are active creators of this very same energy. Through consciously infusing our being with torsion waves of kundalini, we partner with the galactic evolutionary plan being directed from "above" by facilitating our personal enlightenment from "below." This happens as we commit to healing our own duality and begin to operate out of unity consciousness and unconditional love, which gradually resolves conflict and disharmony in all levels of our being—from the genetic up—as we individually return to harmonic identity with Source.

We are not merely passive receivers of evolutionary energy; we are active creators of this very same energy. Through consciously infusing our being with torsion waves of kundalini, we partner with the galactic evolutionary plan being directed from "above" by facilitating our personal enlightenment from "below."

By making the conscious commitment to find ways to attune ourselves to Galactic Center's torsion energy emissions, specifically the tone of Ge that stimulates our

DNA to evolve our lightbody from within, we personally perform the godlike task of ushering in the Age of Consciousness. As inherently spiritual beings with an innate impulse to return home, we are calling to us the very spiritual energies designed to take us there, proving that "As above, so below" can, and should, be read the other way as well: "So below, as above."

This truthful paradox dissolves at a stroke the false opposition between "nature" (above) and "nurture" (below), inviting us to appreciate the intricate evolutionary interplay between the macro- and microcosmic. Just as importantly, this paradox also invites us to surrender any residual belief not only in causality but in our own powerlessness, and embrace a new way of thinking in which a single person in touch with the divinity within can alter the course of history by forging a new reality. "As I do these things, so shall ye do them, and greater things," said Jesus, who also stated, "Nothing will be impossible for you." Acknowledging our inner divinity as a step on the path to embodying it is not to be confused with narcissism or individualism, since we must further admit that everyone's divine birthright is the same limitless creational potential of unconditional love.

As mentioned near the beginning of this book in Chapter One, in *The Isaiah Effect* Braden claims on the basis of his study of one of the Dead Sea Scrolls that the Gnostics from the time of Christ employed a type of prayer called *active prayer* to alter quantum outcomes by changing the pray-er's picture of reality. Active prayer, as Braden describes it, is a type of focused intention that appreciates whatever is being requested as having already occurred.

This is not the place to go into a full explanation of active prayer. I merely wish to point out that active prayer employs five interactive modalities that together are capable of changing quantum outcomes. Braden denominates the first three of these modalities *thought*, *feeling*, and *emotion*. If this trinity is utilized harmoniously and combined with *peace* and *love*, then "our world mirrors the effect of our prayer." Of particular relevance to the Regenetics Method is that these five intercessory modalities (thought, feeling, emotion, peace, and love) correspond kinesiologically to the five nucleotides of DNA and RNA—which, in turn, have been shown to align with the five vowels. This means that when we use language such as prayer or an energized narrative to change reality consciously, we do so through our bodies by activating our divine genetic endowment: our quantum biology.

In a multidimensional reality composed of infinite parallel universes, any of which can suddenly land in our own like a ball bouncing on a roulette wheel, we can change the future by simply, following John English, dreaming the one we want into being. "Rather than *creating* our reality," Braden has suggested, "it may be more accurate to say that we create the conditions into which we *attract future outcomes*, already established, into the focus of the present." Marciniak conceptualizes such Mastery of Intention as "reality adjusting" and understands it as an inherently energetic endeavor: "Refocusing your attention to reinforce the outcome you desire will alter the frequency you transmit, inevitably opening the door to another probable outcome."

Mastery of Intention is a deeply personal process that always occurs in the present. No technology, guru or savior, however advanced, can do for us what only a commitment to evolving and operating out of our own divine consciousness and physiology can achieve. The choice is ours in every now whether to give away our power to something or someone outside ourselves, or to summon the courage, integrity and impeccability to return home by walking the challenging but ultimately enlightening Black Road of Spirit.

APPENDIX A: TESTIMONIALS

[The following Testimonials from clients are for educational purposes only and make no medical claims. The first two Testimonials are by the same person writing soon after Potentiation Electromagnetic Repatterning then just after completing the 42-week process. The last two Testimonials relate to Articulation Bioenergy Enhancement. Additional Testimonials to all phases of the Regenetics Method are available online at http://www.phoenixregenetics.org and http://www.potentiation.net.]

"It hasn't been quite two weeks since I received Potentiation and so many things have already changed. I was really losing ground before Potentiation and felt I would die from complications from pesticide exposure last summer. The night of my session I felt that toxic energy being removed. I was so deeply moved and uplifted I could hardly sleep. The next day brought waves of detoxification but nothing as challenging as having allergic reactions. That morning I had a giant breakthrough and experienced bliss throughout my body for hours. It felt like liquid light was surrounding and flooding my being. My body was peaceful and a new very, very quiet place inside me emerged. I'm sure this quiet place has always been there, but the noise of the war in my body has prevented me from hearing it. Before Potentiation at night I would start to lose motor coordination. Now I can get down the stairs even in the middle of the night without a problem. This is significant because in the past it literally took me hours in the morning to get on my feet. Also, the moles on my neck have faded and half of them are gone. Even my urinary functioning is back to normal where I used to have to strain. I simply cannot thank you enough." DM, Orcas Island, Washington

"I have completed my nine months for the Potentiation process and boy am I happy. I now have a life where before I had only restrictions. I can drive my car without wearing a mask. I can shovel shavings for my horse's stall without feeling dizzy and sick. I can stay on the computer 6 to 8 hours a day instead of less than one hour. I have a great boyfriend. I am well enough to work and earn a good living—something I've waited 15 years for. The person I was before Potentiation was so physically damaged by heavy metal and other toxicity it was just a matter of time before a nasty reaction would have sent me out with heart failure. It's difficult to describe in words, but I feel new and renewed, as if the best part of me expanded and everything else, including my brain fog, just disappeared. My heartfelt thanks." DM, Orcas Island, Washington

"I am so grateful for Potentiation. It has really helped me turn the corner on emotional reactivity in important relationships. In the midst of conflict I am able to both understand the other person and have on-the-spot clarity about my feelings and the needs of the situation, and communicate it, with respect for myself and the other person. It has transformed conflict around here, with lovely effects that have radiated into my extended family, my daughter, my son and my mother." JS, Colorado Springs, Colorado

"I'm in my third month of Potentiation and I wanted to let you know the profound effects it has had on my life already. First of all, I've kept a Potentiation journal, which I feel has helped me maintain positive intention. I've been doing a detox program with my alternative healthcare professional and was aware of the beneficial effects of Potentiation on that program. But what really made it concrete was when I recently did an ionized footbath. I put my hands and feet in a tub of warm water with an ion machine. My practitioner could identify the waste being pulled from my lymph and joints, including heavy metals. What he saw made a believer of him. He said he'd never seen anyone draw out so much 'stuff' so quickly. I could even feel toxicity being pulled out of my brain. It was truly amazing. I'm looking forward to Articulation at the five-month mark, followed by Elucidation. I feel very blessed to work with you both. I feel and know your work is truly transformational." MR, Assumption, Illinois

"Thank you so much for last week's Potentiation session. I've been involved with energy work for a long time and have never experienced the kind of shift that has happened since connecting with you. I've already released a lot of emotional garbage. The amazing thing is that even though it was intense, I felt supported. Physically, in fact, I feel better than I have in years. Since the onset of my chronic environmental illness many years ago, any strong emotion would rattle my nervous system and make my allergies worse. Not now. I feel good. The emotional stuff has cleared. I never really expected to feel completely well again, and it's a little mind-boggling thinking about what I'm going to do with my life as a fully functioning person." SP, Orcas Island, Washington

"I want to tell you about the subtle changes that have been taking place in my life since my Potentiation last week. I'm experiencing an overall calmness and wisdom. My loved ones seem more drawn to be with me. I'm communicating in a more specific and less emotional manner, and have started to just enjoy my time, no matter what I'm doing. I've started observing what 'is' and noticing what does and doesn't work, and am working on re-creating the life I want based purely on my potential. My health is improving every day; I'm definitely more aware of what is and isn't contributing to my wellbeing. It has only been a week since my session, and I realize I have so much more to be, do and have!" JH, Raynham, Massachusetts

"At the time of my Potentiation seven months ago, I was depressed and suicidal due to my inability to sleep. I'd often go whole nights and only get an hour of sleep. I still struggle somewhat with insomnia, but I no longer, or rarely, have the kind of nights I used to have before Potentiation. I've also suffered for years from TMJ, but in spite of braces and a mouth full of metal, I've improved in this area as well. I still have many challenges, but I now generally believe life is worth living and I even have feelings of happiness and joy. I also had a serious case of Restless Leg Syndrome when I began this process. I still have it at times, but lately it has been a lot less. I know this doesn't sound like much, but trust me, it's a big deal. I think of all the many things I've tried, Potentiation has probably been the best investment in my overall health and has helped me the most." KC, Atlanta, Georgia

"I consider myself very open-minded and accept the power of spirit to heal physical and mental imbalances. Yet last year when I was suddenly confronted with severe food and chemical allergies after a trip to Haiti, I felt humbled by limitations I'd never personally experienced. A yoga and meditation practitioner for many years, I thought I was immune to chronic physical ailments. A close friend recommended Potentiation, and since I'd noticed significant improvements in her, I decided to try it. I prepared myself mentally for a week, drawing on my own knowledge of the power of intention to heal. My Potentiation session itself wasn't at first very different from deep meditation. Soon, however, the results were astonishing. In less than two days I felt my allergies completely leave my body, as well as mucus-forming food 'intolerances' to wheat and dairy that had plagued me since childhood. I could eat anything, though I'm still vegetarian for moral reasons, and could finally breathe through my nose again! I strongly recommend this healing process, but be very pure and strong in your intention as to why you're 'potentiating.' Don't forget it's your higher mind you're connecting with, and that healing starts in you." DR, Marshall, North Carolina

"I'm noticing a subtle but powerful shift. The best I can explain it is that the frequency at which I'm vibrating is changing again. I'm definitely moving to a higher vibration. And I feel this is definitely tied in with Potentiation." BK, Asheville, North Carolina

"Thank you for a most graceful entrance into my Potentiation process. I shared the experience with two other people, one receiving Potentiation and one who was seven months into it, and found that the combined energy and intentional bond we formed brought us all to a state of ecstasy. When the session ended, nothing but radiant bliss was pulsing through my body. I felt moved to embrace the person I was sharing the experience with and we both felt the energy magnify. I've been in the holistic field for many years, and Potentiation has been one of the most profound processes I've ever experienced." JC, Novato, California

"I'm definitely feeling a shift since my Potentiation two weeks ago. Many 'stuck wheels' have begun to move again in my life. I feel strangely 'uplifted' from inside out, as if something almost structural is being built. This is accompanied by a sense of stability and support I've never felt before. Prior to my session I felt I was sort of 'crumbling' inside, but now I feel I'm 'rebuilding.' This change is very obvious. Emotionally, I'm doing better than I've done in a very long time. Many issues I've struggled to understand for years have suddenly been made clear to me. I've also gained a more profound awareness of Christ presence through this work. I've worked with the best energy/spiritual healers on the planet over thirty years, and Potentiation definitely rates among them—with the distinct difference that this also feels like something tangible is being constructed. Potentiation is certainly the 'reset' that you call it." LH, Black Mountain, North Carolina

"Since Potentiation I generally have a sense of greater wellbeing, stronger workouts, less sugar and food cravings. I seem to be taking better care of myself, extending myself a certain tenderness, suffering less anxiety. It feels good!" CE, Asheville, North Carolina

"My experience of Potentiation was both subtle and powerful. During the early phase, the first few months, I felt an unusual sense of happiness and peace and an overall subtle shift inside. Then, as the process unfolded, I realized my food allergies had completely disappeared! I'd tried other treatments with limited success, but with Potentiation I gradually noticed I could enjoy food that would have normally caused headaches and spaciness. Very remarkable!" EL, Asheville, North Carolina

"What do I feel is different since last week's Potentiation? There will be a big layoff soon where I work, but I feel much lighter, calmer and more positive. A lot of my depression is gone. Also, for the last couple years I've felt the left side of my body tightening and I've constantly had the urge to stretch it. One doctor said I had Illio Tibial Syndrome and gave me stretches to do. A massage therapist/instructor said I had a fascia problem. Being treated by them helped very little. I underwent other unusual therapies, also with little results. But now I've had a major shift and tremendous release on my left side, especially in the left hip and leg. I really cannot believe it. My hip is so loose, lighter feeling and rounded out. I do massage therapy and for years have worked on myself. But now there is no need to work on these areas!" CH, Streamwood, Illinois

"Since initiating the Potentiation process 4 months ago, I've experienced several rather profound changes. My hot flashes have subsided, which is a real relief and allows me to sleep better at night. Most of the arthritis in my hands and knees has cleared up, reducing my dependence on glucosamine. I've gone through some detoxification and can sense more energy coming in through my chakras." PD, Myrtle Beach, South Carolina

"Since my Potentiation I feel great! I have loads of energy and generally feel balanced. During and just prior to my session last week, I felt immensely relaxed, deeply tranquil. This afternoon I plan to go jogging. I have strength that I haven't felt in quite some time. Thank you so much for sharing your healing work with me and humanity." AA, Asheville, North Carolina

"My Potentiation session was a transformative experience. I felt a deep connection, sort of the way one can feel an acupuncture needle activating a meridian point. I also felt, and continue to feel, a kind of turning of the mind away from negativity, an enhanced ability to move out of, or not fall into, what I call 'bowling alley gutter mind.'" ET, North Hampton, Massachusetts

"Thanks for the wonderful Potentiation session last evening. I felt an armor (with lock and key) lift off my heart area with lots of emotional release. The emotion of FRUSTRATION kept coming up along with a HUGE wave of energy starting with my head, heart, stomach and root chakra areas. I am very grateful for your wonderful healing abilities." CS, Atlanta, Georgia

"Thank you so, so much for all your help! You've truly been a blessing from God. The day after Potentiation, my chronic rash disappeared 99.99%. The only thing that seemed to hang with me was a few small spots that only had an irritated sensation on an occasional basis. I feel that these spots are only energy vents, clearing out old residue. All in all I feel GREAT! The positive energy I feel has continually gone in a forward healing mode, which has been so exciting. THANK YOU SO MUCH!" LM, Sylva, North Carolina

"My daughter was so pleased with her Potentiation results I had to try it. I had severe food allergies that had escalated through the years to the point where I could barely eat anything without discomfort. Within the first month after Potentiation, I found myself able to add more foods to my diet. It has now been two months since my session, and I feel I've improved at least 70%. I'm 82 years old and to see my health improve so fast is thrilling." LH, Sylva, North Carolina

"Since my session I've felt wonderful. I've been trying several therapies, but I know Potentiation has been the catalyst for any real healing. I just attended an amazing lecture by Dr. Len Horowitz, who explained how DNA is really just an antenna to receive love and light from the Creator, that all healing comes from these higher energies, and that when our DNA gets clouded with chemicals, toxicity and negativity, it shuts off our connection with the universe and ability to heal ourselves." SM, Denver, Colorado

"Following my Articulation I'm experiencing huge waves of energy. Additionally, I've had big energetic openings that relate to the second and fourth chakras—physical energies shifting as well as beliefs and emotions. I'm definitely moving into more of a 'third-person' awareness, which is kind of a surprise in the midst of all these powerful awakenings. I've also had lots of mostly positive movement in the relationship area. Strangely enough, with all of this going on I feel I'm definitely moving to a place of internal stability and balance. This is truly some powerful work!" TV, Cincinnati, Ohio

"I felt and continue to feel the Articulation more profoundly and consciously than the Potentiation. It feels very deep but also gentle and nonintrusive. I have been meditating for 13 years and have historically found it difficult to carry the consciousness of my meditative states into my everyday life. So I have often felt like two people. Since Articulation I feel more present, more incarnated, and more like one person. Interestingly, my son developed a fever within a few hours of the Articulation. He was asleep by the time of our session and I didn't check on him until much later, so I don't know if he developed the fever immediately. But he looks wonderful and lighter, as if some burden a five-year-old should not have has been lifted from him. Something wonderful is happening." AM, Phoenixville, Pennsylvania

APPENDIX B:
FREQUENTLY ASKED QUESTIONS

Q: What distinguishes the Regenetics Method from other DNA activation techniques?
A: Those with highly evolved consciousness such as spiritual teachers have always insisted that the body-mind-spirit can be healed by words in the form of songs, poems, prayers, affirmations, or mantras. The sound of the words must be harmonically attuned to the organism and the intention behind them impeccable. This is why although DNA activation has become trendy, results can vary enormously—ranging from none to life-changing. The more advanced the facilitator's consciousness, the less need there is for mechanical devices. Some shamanic healers believe that the digital recording is like a clone— lacking spirit—which calls into question the effectiveness of DNA activation CDs. This touches on a discussion of the Path of Technology (giving away one's power to a technological intermediary) vs. the Path of Nature (self-empowerment or mastery), but the bottom line is: *there is no substitute for live human consciousness and voice.* In addition, we are aware of no other DNA activation modality specifically designed to seal and heal the Fragmentary Body. This is a key point because without bridging duality at the level of the bioenergy fields, it is impossible to build a stable evolutionary vehicle or higher energy body. We have performed Regenetics sessions for

many individuals who have experienced prior DNA activation, and the typical response has been that what we do is uniquely powerful and effective. Finally, the Regenetics Method employs the recently rediscovered Solfeggio scale. The Solfeggio is a primoridal six-note scale many scholars believe to be the creational scale. This scale is so transformational it was hidden by the Roman church for centuries. One of the Solfeggio notes, "Mi," is a frequency that has been used by molecular biologists to repair genetic defects. This is also the principle note used in Potentiation Electromagnetic Repatterning.

Q: Do you suggest any activities or resources that may support the physical body while experiencing the Regenetics Method?

A: Our own experience has been that drinking several quarts per day of pure water and eating organic food (including starches for toxicity binding) greatly supported our process. This was especially true after our nutritional sensitivities and allergies disappeared following Potentiation Electromagnetic Repatterning. Also, light exercise such as rebounding, swimming and walking is an excellent way to keep the blood and lymph moving to increase oxygenation and assist detoxification. In addition, we found exposure to natural sunlight in moderation very energizing and healing. Finally, sleep as required by the body is deeply restorative.

Q: Does Potentiation change my basic DNA?

A: No. Potentiation Electromagnetic Repatterning activates a latent potential in DNA designed to "reset" the human bioenergy blueprint so that it resonates at a higher vibratory frequency more in harmony with the torsion energy emissions of Source—at which point the individual can utilize greater amounts of life energy and evolve a "conscious biology" ultimately capable of embodying unity consciousness.

Q: Do I have to fully understand the Regenetics Method for it to work?

A: Absolutely not. The Regenetics Method is an experiential, not intellectual, process. Parents have reported very positive results in young children, for example. Few people "understand" the medicines they try. That said, the more one commits to thinking in this new way about human potential and the ability to re-create ourselves at the "ener-genetic" level, the more one can engage through intention in the process of conscious personal mastery as a bio-spiritual path to becoming "whole."

Q: Do you need a bloodspot or other personal item such as a photograph to activate my DNA?

A: No. Only your name, date of birth, permission and intention are required. The latter two are assumed on scheduling your session and receipt of your educational service fee. Mutual intention establishes an "ener-genetic" connection on the "biological Internet" constituted by DNA, allowing DNA activation to be "emailed" to the correct recipient. In the case of responsible adults, we never perform a Regenetics session without an individual's conscious permission.

Q: Do you need to know my symptoms, medical diagnoses or other issues to activate my DNA?
A: Symptoms, medical diagnoses and related issues are unnecessary on our end. What is important is that you clearly set your own goals, as you will be the one integrating the energies of Regenetics over the weeks and months following your session(s). By focusing on conscious personal mastery as a path of healing or "wholing," the Regenetics Method represents a purposeful shift away from the diagnostic model. In many cases diagnosis oversimplifies complex processes while "locking in" a problem in the sufferer's mind. We have moved away from the diagnostic model after realizing there are many "nonlocal" factors at work in genuine healing that transcend the often limited perspective of left-brain analysis. The most important factor in determining the level of success of the Regenetics Method is the individual's degree of conscious intention to use these energies for mastery in walking one's highest path in life. This means making a commitment to evolve in the direction of unity consciousness. We are not saying you must completely believe in the process for it to bear fruit, but we do insist that your willingness to approach your "ener-genetic" unfoldment with an open mind and especially heart greatly influences your experience of Regenetics.

Q: If you don't know what's wrong with me, how can you help me?
A: One of the fundamental precepts behind the Regenetics Method is that all illness, whether "physiological" or "psychological," arises from disharmonies in the body's bioenergy fields. Similar

conclusions have been reached by a growing number of scientists, including UCLA professor Valerie Hunt (author of *Infinite Mind*) and physician Richard Gerber (author of *Vibrational Medicine*). Through kinesiological (muscle) testing, we have observed an extraordinary level of consistency of energy patterns in the electromagnetic fields and corresponding *chakras* of particular groups. Each "Electromagnetic Group" possesses a unique arrangement in its bioenergy blueprint that applies to all members. This is an exciting discovery because it renders individualized diagnosis unnecessary. To "potentiate" a person, we simply use surrogate muscle testing to determine the Electromagnetic Group and then apply the appropriate DNA activation.

Q: Is there anything I can do on my end besides putting myself in a "co-creative" state to assist my DNA activation?
A: Definitely. The single most important thing you can do to assist your DNA activation is to open your heart and operate with love in all areas of your life. Exciting new genetic research by Dr. Glen Rein reveals that love and related emotions such as joy and compassion "decompress" DNA so that RNA can access codes for healing. On the other hand, fear, anger, depression and even boredom "compress" DNA, causing it to close down on itself and limiting the individual's ability to heal. We also recommend that you take time before your session(s) to clarify your intention by specifying (preferably in writing) the areas you want to work on. Keeping a "Regenetics journal" in the weeks and months following your session(s) is also a good way to stay focused on your transformation. Your intention is extremely powerful and

important in actualizing the energies of the Regenetics Method—although you will receive them in any case because the simple gesture of scheduling a session is a form of intention. During the session(s) focus on the areas you want to address and imagine "downloading" healing energies into the places that need them. Your goal should be to vitalize those areas that will allow you to reach your full potential. You can continue to clarify your intention on a daily basis, by journaling or otherwise. It is also a good idea to remain open to serendipity and trust your intuition, as other modalities that present themselves may assist your unfoldment.

Q: How are Regenetics sessions performed at a distance if they involve sound?

A: Sound in higher dimensions is a standing spiral wave (a form of nonlocal torsion energy or universal creative consciousness) that, according to recent research in Russia by the Gariaev group, can be transmitted instantaneously across theoretically infinite distances via DNA. This research demonstrates that DNA constitutes a "biocomputer network" similar to the Internet that, being present anywhere, is simultaneously present everywhere— effectively doing away with distance. In *Reinventing Medicine* Dr. Larry Dossey makes a very strong case for nonlocal approaches to healing, noting that many scientific "studies reveal that healing can be achieved at a distance by directing loving and compassionate thoughts, intentions, and prayers to others, who may even be unaware" of such efforts. Our decision to perform Regenetics sessions remotely is partly based on convenience; it allows us to touch people's lives wherever they are. In addition, remote healing invites one to "think outside the box" of what we have been taught about the body and realize that, "ener-genetically," humans are unlimited.

Q: Does the Regenetics Method involve anything resembling witchcraft or voodoo?

A: Regenetics is a method of DNA activation. Many of our clients are deeply religious. The Regenetics Method is based on many accepted and emerging scientific theories relative to higher-dimensional sound and intention, nonlocalized mind, and the ability to activate the self-repair potential in "junk" DNA. Our research has centered on the impact of sound and intention (the two principal differentiated forms of torsion Source energy) on this "junk" DNA that has until recently been considered useless. For an enlightening new take on "junk" DNA, which we propose renaming *potential DNA*, see "Genetics Beyond Genes" in the November 2003 issue of *Scientific American*. Our approach has involved kinesiology (muscle testing) to map the structure of the human electromagnetic fields. For more information on kinesiology, see David Hawkins, M.D., Ph.D., *Power vs. Force*.

Q: How does DNA relate to the body's bioenergy fields?

A: The latest research in "wave-genetics" likens DNA to a "biocomputer" that holographically projects the electromagnetic human bioenergy fields, which in turn regulate cellular metabolism and replication. This new research flies in the face of traditional molecular biology dogma that considers DNA merely a biochemical protein-assembly code. In a superb article entitled "From Helix to

Hologram," longtime genetics researchers Iona Miller and Richard Alan Miller write, "Life is fundamentally electromagnetic rather than chemical, the DNA blueprint functioning as a biohologram which serves as a guiding matrix for organizing physical form." The Gariaev group has demonstrated it is possible to use radio and light waves, or sound combined with intention (words), to activate DNA, which then can modify the human electromagnetic fields. These fields, in turn, are capable of modifying how cells are made and function. We call this noninvasive approach that represents the exciting confluence of energy medicine and molecular biology Regenetics.

Q: Why in your opinion do traditional energy clearing techniques often fail to produce lasting results?
A: Traditional energy clearings work through the nervous and meridian system as opposed to DNA. But geneticists have begun to refer to DNA, not the nervous system, as our "biocomputer." In order to "reset" the human bioenergy blueprint and restore it to harmonic functioning, it is necessary to go directly to the root of the malfunction—which can only be accomplished by way of the genetic code. To do this noninvasively, one can employ higher-dimensional sound and intention (torsion energy) to activate the self-healing mechanism in DNA. DNA, then, can revitalize the human electromagnetic fields, and the electromagnetic fields, in turn, are capable of revitalizing the organism.

Q: Is there any 24-hour avoidance period of foods or other substances following Potentiation as there is with NAET® and its derivatives?
A: None.

Q: Will the Regenetics Method interfere with any other energetic methods I might be trying?
A: To the contrary, the Regenetics Method may make other modalities more effective. This applies not only to energetic therapies but to any therapy. Whether to try other modalities following Regenetics is entirely up to you. Always trust your intuition. You, and only you, know what is right for your body, mind, and spirit. Our only caveat is that you ask other practitioners to treat you very gingerly, as the "sealing" of the Fragmentary Body that occurs at approximately the five-month mark of Potentiation Electromagnetic Repatterning allows your bioenergetic system to accomplish more with less energy input.

Q: Does the Regenetics Method work like radionics?
A: Although the Regenetics Method was partly inspired by certain aspects of radionics, the remote energy transmission used in Regenetics should not be confused with radionics. Instead of frequencies broadcast through the astral "psi-field" by way of a mechanical instrument to the client's nervous system, the Regenetics Method employs particular vocalized sounds combined with non-directed healing intentions that work together to transmit an "energized narrative" via the "morphogenetic" Internet constituted by DNA.

Q: I come from a homeopathic background and wonder if Potentiation Electromagnetic Repatterning addresses miasms?
A: Miasms, a focal concept in traditional homeopathy, are paraphysical disease potentials latent in humans that are exploitable through toxic, nutritive, genetic, mental and emotional manipulation of the protein structures (nucleotides) of DNA and RNA. Barbara Hand Clow describes miasms as "etheric masses that hold memory of genetic or past-life diseases that were not cleared due to vaccinations, which prevented ... manifesting the disease memory and erasing it; or memory of disease [driven deeply into the body] by ... antibiotics, chemicals or radiation." Potentiation Electromagnetic Repatterning is designed to begin the process of transmuting this negative "karma" and revitalizing areas damaged by miasms.

Q: Are there any dangers or contraindications involved with the Regenetics Method?
A: There are no dangers. As for contraindications, there are no "indications." Regenetics is not a therapy but a method of facilitating conscious personal mastery. While making no medical claims, we suggest there is every reason to believe, based on hard science, that a successful "reset" of the electromagnetic disharmonies that have created problems can have a profoundly beneficial impact.

Q: Why does Potentiation Electromagnetic Repatterning take nine months to unfold?
A: It takes just over nine months for Potentiation to repattern the electromagnetic blueprint and fill it with torsion Source energy because this process is keyed to the physical density of the body and is subject to its timeline.

The body is wise and knows exactly what to do when its DNA is functioning harmonically. We think of Potentiation Electromagnetic Repatterning as a "rebirth cycle," making the nine-month (42-week) period most appropriate.

Q: Does the Regenetics Method take care of Candida?

A: A popular misconception even in the alternative health community is that Candida is "bad." Nothing could be further from the truth. *Candida albicans* is one of several important microorganisms in the body that are saprophytic, meaning it consumes dead and toxic tissue, and when it proliferates it is actually trying to cleanse not harm the body. Candida overgrowth problems tend to lessen gradually as the body detoxifies. This makes perfect sense because as toxicity levels decline, there is less reason for Candida to proliferate systemically. "Candida cleans the system by eating accumulated [toxins] in the tissues," writes health researcher and nutritionist Aajonus Vonderplanitz. "Candida is helpful and should have its cycle. The worst thing anyone could do if he or she wants to improve his or her health is to destroy Candida."

Q: What do you see as the relationship between the electromagnetic fields and the *chakras*?

A: Chakras are bioenergy centers in the form of wheels running vertically along the spinal column and head. In the Regenetics Method, the chakra system is progressively activated, leading to increased bioenergy output and availability. Each of the principal chakras corresponds numerically to an electromagnetic field, and functions in tandem with that field, such that the first or "root" chakra aligns with the first field, the second or "sex" chakra aligns with the second field, etc. Together, the chakras (which process higher-dimensional torsion energy in the form of light) and electromagnetic fields (which process higher-dimensional torsion energy in the form of sound) establish the holographic interface that gives rise to the human body. Utilizing the genetic sound-light translation mechanism, each sonic field energizes the corresponding chakra with higher-dimensional light, which then transfers as bioenergy or *kundalini* to specific aspects of the subtle anatomy. The majority of elements governed by a particular electromagnetic field also apply to the corresponding chakra.

Q: Does everyone benefit from the Regenetics Method?

A: We have had the opportunity to work with people from a variety of backgrounds and beliefs. Some clients have had more profound results than others. It seems that anyone approaching this work with a truly open mind and heart experiences a positive shift, even if it was not what was expected. We advise that you set your intention firmly and specifically on what you want to achieve, then trust in the wisdom of your DNA as you go about living with joy. A good way to maintain your intention is to journal and/or pray and/or meditate regularly on your own conscious personal mastery (your particular evolutionary path). Your mind is extremely powerful, so use it to create a healthier reality. Finally, we cannot overemphasize the importance of inviting more and more love into all levels of your being, as this makes your DNA available for activation and transformation.

Q: Can someone who is already healthy receive benefits from Regenetics?

A: How do you define "healthy"? For us, *healthy* describes someone who is "whole" in every way: physically, mentally, emotionally, and spiritually. Sadly, from this perspective, few people today are healthy. Clients with no physical problems often report healing on a mental or emotional level. Others experience the Regenetics Method more palpably. No two individuals are alike, but most clients (even those who consider themselves healthy) report positive shifts in one or more areas.

Q: I've been reading about the healing power of *kundalini* and am interested in Articulation Bioenergy Enhancement. Is it possible to receive Articulation without having done Potentiation?

A: Typically, no. On rare occasions, we have worked with individuals who have already succeeded in "sealing" their Fragmentary Body, making it possible to skip Potentiation and move directly to Articulation. Generally speaking, however, Potentiation is the primary DNA activation that makes Articulation (as well as Elucidation) possible. One needs to be at the five-month mark of Potentiation or beyond in order to benefit from Articulation. Elucidation is then appropriate after the 42-week Potentiation cycle has completed. Articulation and Elucidation can be performed later than this minimum timeline—without diminishing their effectiveness—but not earlier.

Q: How do I know if the Regenetics Method is right for me?

A: Trust your intuition. We live in a world based largely on denying our own power. The Regenetics Method involves experiencing firsthand the transformational truth that the only real power exists inside you. If you are afraid to change, feel locked in victim consciousness, believe that anyone besides yourself can ultimately heal you, or are addicted to old illness or relational patterns, Regenetics is probably not for you—at this time. If, however, the concept of conscious personal mastery excites you; you are committed to your own empowerment; you believe it is possible to transcend limitation; and the Regenetics Method resonates with you, go for it!

Q: Is it possible for me to "mess up" my Potentiation Electromagnetic Repatterning?

A: As long as you approach your Potentiation with an open mind and heart, we know of no way you can "mess up" your DNA activation and electromagnetic repatterning. This includes exposure to other forms of DNA activation, other types of energy work, and even environmental radiation sources such as computers and cell phones.

Q: Do I need to commit to the full Regenetics Method to maximize my benefits?

A: Although many of our clients have benefited greatly from only Potentiation or only Potentiation combined with Articulation, we strongly recommend that you consider committing to the full Regenetics Method as a path of conscious personal mastery. Such a commitment represents a more powerfully energized intention that appears to have a more profound impact on the individual's DNA activation and unfoldment. That said, there is certainly nothing wrong with trying Potentiation

Electromagnetic Repatterning first before determining whether to move forward with the process.

Q: Do you offer a sliding scale or other discounts for your services?

A: We typically do not discount our fees as we feel they are more than fair for the unique services we provide. We do offer a special discounted fee for individuals who commit to the full Regenetics Method. In addition, we perform sessions free of charge for children under twelve as long as at least one parent or guardian is willing to experience the same session by paying our normal fee. Parents have reported significant benefits even in very young children, who by nature experience the Regenetics Method less cognitively and more intuitively than adults.

Q: Do you ever perform sessions for groups?

A: Yes. We often work with couples and even whole families. Doing a collective session is not only capable of facilitating individual issues but also of working "morphogenetically" to heal one-on-one and group relational dynamics. We are also open to doing sessions for larger groups.

Q: How do I get started?

A: Email or telephone us using the contact information listed on our websites: http://www.phoenixregenetics.org and http://www.potentiation.net.

APPENDIX C: SAMPLE ELECTROMAGNETIC GROUP

This Appendix provides a simplified Schematic of the first Electromagnetic Group encountered by the developers of the Regenetics Method. There are twelve such groups in total corresponding to the twelve pairs of cranial nerves, suggesting that the twelve groups together comprise the collective Mind of humanity. Following Potentiation Electromagnetic Repatterning, during which surrogate muscle testing is employed to determine the correct group, clients receive a similarly detailed Schematic of the particular Electromagnetic Group to which they belong.

Each of the nine lower electromagnetic fields represents a gestalt or "ecosystem" where a number of elements interrelate either harmoniously to produce vitality or disharmoniously to create disease. In the latter case, dysfunction in a particular field can, but does not necessarily, result in one of several Focal Conditions. These Focal Conditions represent *generalized potentials only* for the Electromagnetic Group and may have nothing whatsoever to do with an individual's situation. Blanks (—) indicate no applicable energy for the category. *This information is solely for educational purposes and is not intended to diagnose any medical condition or recommend any medical treatment, medication, or supplement.*

It will be noted there is a tenth field labeled the Master (Source) Field. This is the unified field of the soul or Higher Self that is not subject to fragmentation or disease and is and always has been "whole." In a profound sense, Potentiation Electromagnetic Repatterning is designed as the first step in assisting individuals to unite this Source field with their lower fields, a transformational process that continues with Articulation Bioenergy Enhancement and culminates in Elucidation Triune Activation. The ultimate goal is to follow this path of conscious personal mastery to complete bio-spiritual healing/enlightenment.

There is nothing the client is expected to "do" with the information contained in this Schematic, which is primarily intended to help "ground" Potentiation and the Regenetics Method with specific data and a Timeline relative to each field. For example, in the event of emotional release, by referencing the Schematic, it may be possible to determine whether the emotions in question relate to the electromagnetic field currently being energized by torsion waves (universal creative consciousness). Included are concepts from many disciplines ranging from allopathic medicine and homeopathy to Chinese medicine and astrology that function within the electromagnetic blueprint and may or may not assist with understanding—depending on the individual's orientation and background. *It is unnecessary to understand all the terms contained in this Schematic, which is purposefully designed to meet you at your level.*

The Regenetics Method recognizes that the human bioenergy fields are primary in creating health or disease, an idea substantiated by recent research in "wave-genetics" proving that cellular functions are regulated not just biochemically but bioenergetically. Therefore, it is helpful to "map" these fields in order to understand them individually and in holistic relationship to one another. This is an empowering approach to grasping the complexity of the human organism across the body-mind-spirit continuum, as opposed to seeing ourselves as limited physical beings.

The order presented in this Schematic charts the flow of torsion energy from the Master Field through the nine electromagnetic fields which Potentiation initiates. Starting with the ninth field, "potentiators" spend an average of ten days in each field on the way "down" (9-1), then approximately seven days per field on the way back "up" (meaning a total of seventeen days in the first field as the torsion waves reverse direction). Once the ninth field is reached again, there follows a transitional period of two weeks or so as the number of fields recalibrates from nine to eight in number. During this period, the ninth field literally descends and fuses with the second field, creating an "infinity circuit" that makes possible the four-month "charging" phase when each field from the eighth down slowly fills with Source-derived torsion energy much like a tiered fountain as shown in Figure 4.

FIELD: Master (Source)
CHAKRA: —
PERMANENT ATOM: Atmic
SUBTLE BODY: Soul
GLAND: —
BRAINWAVE: —
GENETIC COMPONENT: —
CELLULAR ASPECT: —
ORGAN SYSTEM: Nadis
MERIDIAN: —

MIASM: —
PRIMARY TOXIN: —
MICROORGANISM POPULATION: —
EMOTIONS: Gratitude, Hope, Joy, Love
FOCAL CONDITION: —
NUTRIENT: —
CELL SALTS: Calcium Fluoride, Kali Phosphate
TREE OF LIFE: Nezah/Eternity
ACTIVE PRAYER MODALITY: —
PLANETS: Mars, Venus
SIGNS: Aries, Libra
SHAPES: Tetrahedron, Merkabah, Star of David
COLOR: —

ELECTROMAGNETIC FIELD: 9
CHAKRA: 9
PERMANENT ATOM: —
SUBTLE BODY: Spiritual
GLANDS: Salivary
BRAINWAVE: —
GENETIC COMPONENT: DNA
CELLULAR ASPECT: —
ORGAN SYSTEMS: Autonomic Nervous System, Gall Bladder, Liver
MERIDIAN: Liver/Gall Bladder
MIASM: —
PRIMARY TOXIN: —
MICROORGANISM POPULATION: —
EMOTIONS: Atonement, Deprivation, Resentment, Sense of Being Trapped, Unforgiveness
FOCAL CONDITIONS: Anemia, Creutzfeld-Jakob Disease, MS, Neurosis, Parkinson Disease
NUTRIENTS: Hydrogen, Nitrogen, Sulfur
CELL SALT: Natrium Mur
TREE OF LIFE: Yesod/Foundation
ACTIVE PRAYER MODALITY: —

PLANET: Sun
SIGNS: Leo, Ophiuchus
SHAPES: Parallelogram, Rhombus
COLOR: Orange

ELECTROMAGNETIC FIELD: 8
CHAKRA: 8
PERMANENT ATOM: —
SUBTLE BODY: Spiritual (Lightbody)
GLANDS: Hypothalamus, Lacrimal
BRAINWAVE: —
GENETIC COMPONENT: Mitochondrial DNA
CELLULAR ASPECTS: Cell Functions, Cell Parts
ORGAN SYSTEM: Sinus/Limbic
MERIDIANS: Central Vessel, Governing Vessel
MIASM: —
PRIMARY TOXIN: —
MICROORGANISM POPULATION: —
EMOTIONS: Despair, Grief, Guilt, Melancholy, Yearning
FOCAL CONDITIONS: Depression, Sinusitis, Seasonal Affective Disorder
NUTRIENTS: Potassium, Salt, Sodium, Trace Minerals
CELL SALT: Kali Mur
TREE OF LIFE: Keter/Crown, Hokhmah/Wisdom
ACTIVE PRAYER MODALITY: —
PLANETS: Earth, Moon
SIGNS: Capricornus, Scorpius
SHAPE: Cross
COLOR: Indigo

ELECTROMAGNETIC FIELD: 7
CHAKRA: 7
PERMANENT ATOM: Mental
SUBTLE BODY: Mental
GLAND: Parathyroid
BRAINWAVE: Gamma

GENETIC COMPONENTS: Cytosine, RNA
CELLULAR ASPECTS: Cell Division, Krebs Cycle
ORGAN SYSTEMS: Bladder/Kidney/Urinary, Musculoskeletal
MERIDIAN: Bladder/Kidney
MIASMS: Vaccination, Will
PRIMARY TOXINS: Antibiotics, Chem Trails, Fluoride, Root Canal Toxins, Vaccines
MICROORGANISM POPULATION: Intestinal Flora
EMOTIONS: Apathy, Disappointment, Discouragement, Disillusionment, Frustration, Helplessness, Hopelessness, Lack of Faith, Stress
FOCAL CONDITIONS: ADD/ADHD, AIDS, Arthritis, Autism, Avian Flu, Cavitation, CIFDS, Fibromyalgia, Gulf War Syndrome, Incontinence, Leukemia, Lupus, Multiple Chemical Sensitivity, Osteoporosis, Scoliosis, SARS, SIDS
NUTRIENTS: Boron, Calcium, Ionic Calcium, Ferrous Sulphate, Iron, Magnesium, Vitamin D, Vitamin D3
CELL SALTS: Magnesium Phosphate, Natrium Sulphate
TREE OF LIFE: Hesed/Mercy
ACTIVE PRAYER MODALITY: Thought
PLANETS: Saturn, Vulcan
SIGN: Pisces
SHAPE: Circle
COLOR: Blue

ELECTROMAGNETIC FIELD: 6
CHAKRA: 6
PERMANENT ATOM: Astral
SUBTLE BODY: Mental
GLANDS: Sweat
BRAINWAVE: Theta
GENETIC COMPONENT: Adenine
CELLULAR ASPECTS: Mesoderm, Morula, Tunica Media
ORGAN SYSTEMS: Dermal, Inner Ear, Mucous Membrane, Respiratory
MERIDIAN: Lung

MIASMS: Psora, Tuberculosis
PRIMARY TOXINS: Airborne Allergens, Bacterial Toxins, Heavy Metals, Metallic Dental Materials
MICROORGANISM POPULATION: Bacteria, Mycobacteria, Mycoplasmas, Spiroplasmas
EMOTIONS: —
FOCAL CONDITIONS: Acne, Asthma, Eczema, Psychosis, Psoriasis, Suffocation, Tinnitus, Vertigo
NUTRIENTS: Iodine, Molybdenum, Vitamin B, Vitamin B12
CELL SALT: Calcium Sulphate
TREE OF LIFE: Tiferet/Beauty
ACTIVE PRAYER MODALITY: Love
PLANET: Mercury
SIGN: Gemini
SHAPES: Half-circle, Hexagon
COLOR: Green

ELECTROMAGNETIC FIELD: 5
CHAKRA: 5
PERMANENT ATOM: Buddhic/Christ
SUBTLE BODY: Emotional
GLAND: Pituitary
BRAINWAVE: Alpha
GENETIC COMPONENT: Thymine
CELLULAR ASPECTS: Blastula, Endoderm, Tunica Intima
ORGAN SYSTEM: Circulatory
MERIDIANS: Heart, Pericardium
MIASMS: Syphilitic, Thuja Focal
PRIMARY TOXINS: Hydrocarbons, Chlorinated Hydrocarbons
MICROORGANISM POPULATION: Homeostatic Soil Organisms
EMOTIONS: Ambition, Desire, Lust
FOCAL CONDITIONS: Hemophilia, Hot Flashes, Hypertension, Wilson Disease
NUTRIENTS: Manganese, Selenium, Vitamin E, Zinc
CELL SALT: Silicea

TREE OF LIFE: Malkhut/Kingdom
ACTIVE PRAYER MODALITY: Emotion
PLANET: Chiron
SIGN: Sagittarius
SHAPE: Trapezium
COLOR: Red

ELECTROMAGNETIC FIELD: 4
CHAKRA: 4
PERMANENT ATOM: —
SUBTLE BODY: Emotional
GLAND: Pineal
BRAINWAVE: Beta
GENETIC COMPONENT: Guanine
CELLULAR ASPECTS: Ectoderm, Gastrula, Tunica Externa
ORGAN SYSTEMS: Brain, Central Nervous, Optical
MERIDIAN: Triple Heater
MIASMS: Gonorrhea, Psychotic
PRIMARY TOXINS: Artificial Sweeteners, Cooked Food Toxins, Food Additives, Food Colorings, Genetically Modified Organisms, Processed Sugars
MICROORGANISM POPULATION: Yeasts
EMOTIONS: Abandonment, Arrogance, Betrayal, Confusion, Pride, Rejection
FOCAL CONDITIONS: ALS, Alzheimer Disease, Cataracts, Diabetes, Dyslexia, Encephalitis, Food Allergies, Glaucoma, Hypoglycemia, Insomnia, Migraine, Obsessive-compulsive Disorder
NUTRIENTS: Chromium, Methionine, Vanadium, Vitamin K
CELL SALT: Kali Sulphate
TREE OF LIFE: Daat/Knowledge
ACTIVE PRAYER MODALITY: Feeling
PLANET: Jupiter
SIGN: Aquarius
SHAPE: Triangle
COLOR: Turquoise

ELECTROMAGNETIC FIELD: 3
CHAKRAS: 3, Pranic Triangle
PERMANENT ATOM: Physical
SUBTLE BODY: Physical
GLANDS: Adrenal, Thymus
BRAINWAVE: Delta
GENETIC COMPONENT: Uracil
CELLULAR ASPECT: Embryo
ORGAN SYSTEM: Immune
MERIDIAN: Spleen
MIASMS: Cancer, Radiation
PRIMARY TOXINS: Chemicals, Mechanized Fields, Pharmaceuticals, Radioactive Metals, Recreational Drugs, Smoke, Solvents
MICROORGANISM POPULATION: Viruses
EMOTIONS: Anxiety, Fear, Lack of Trust, Panic, Terror, Worry
FOCAL CONDITIONS: Cancer, Paranoia
NUTRIENT: Vitamin C
CELL SALT: Calcium Phosphate
TREE OF LIFE: Hod/Reverberation
ACTIVE PRAYER MODALITY: Peace
PLANET: Pluto
SIGN: Virgo
SHAPE: Crescent
COLORS: Onyx, Purple

ELECTROMAGNETIC FIELD: 2 (the Fragmentary Body)
CHAKRA: 2
PERMANENT ATOM: —
SUBTLE BODY: (Physical)
GLAND: Thyroid
BRAINWAVE: —
GENETIC COMPONENT: —
CELLULAR ASPECT: —
ORGAN SYSTEMS: Mouth/Teeth/Tongue, Reproductive

MERIDIAN: —
MIASM: —
PRIMARY TOXIN: Parasitic Toxins
MICROORGANISM POPULATIONS: Dental Bacteria, Parasites
EMOTIONS: Envy, Jealousy, Shame
FOCAL CONDITIONS: Dental Decay, Halitosis, Impotence, Parasitic Infection, Reproductive System Illness, Sterility
NUTRIENT: Folic Acid
CELL SALT: Natrium Phosphate
TREE OF LIFE: Gevurah/Judgment
ACTIVE PRAYER MODALITY: —
PLANET: Uranus
SIGN: Taurus
SHAPE: Rectangle
COLOR: Yellow

ELECTROMAGNETIC FIELD: 1
CHAKRA: 1
PERMANENT ATOM: —
SUBTLE BODY: Physical
GLAND: Parotid
BRAINWAVE: —
GENETIC COMPONENT: —
CELLULAR ASPECT: —
ORGAN SYSTEMS: Digestive, Pancreatic
MERIDIANS: Large Intestine, Small Intestine, Stomach
MIASM: —
PRIMARY TOXIN: Mycotoxins (from fungal overgrowths)
MICROORGANISM POPULATION: Fungi
EMOTIONS: Anger, Disgust, Hatred, Rage
FOCAL CONDITIONS: Acid Reflux, Colitis, Crohn Disease, Irritable Bowel Syndrome, Leaky Gut
NUTRIENTS: Vitamin A, Vitamin F, Vitamin P
CELL SALT: Ferrum Phosphate
TREE OF LIFE: Binah/Understanding
ACTIVE PRAYER MODALITY: —

PLANET: Neptune
SIGN: Cancer
SHAPES: Sphere, Square
COLOR: Brown

GLOSSARY OF TERMS

[The following list of definitions is intended for reference to assist with understanding the more technical aspects of this book. This Glossary may also be read in its entirety as a "journey in consciousness" through a series of related ideas. Note that 1) most capitalized words and phrases have their own separate definitions and 2) many of the terms listed are, for practical purposes, synonyms.]

Active Prayer: phrase used by Gregg Braden in *The Isaiah Effect* to describe a "prayer technology" employed by the Essenes from the time of Christ. Active Prayer is designed to affect, and effect, quantum outcomes by changing the pray-er's picture of reality through focused intention that validates whatever one is praying for as having already happened. The five intercessory modalities used in Active Prayer—thought, feeling, emotion, peace, and love—correspond to the five Nucleotides of DNA and RNA. The Nucleotides, in turn, align with the five vowels. Thus when we change reality through linguistically expressed intention, we do so via our bodies by activating our divine genetic endowment.

Adam Kadmon: kabalistic name for the fully activated Lightbody based on the tripartite Tetrahedron shape and the Merkabah. The Adam Kadmon represents the complete unfolding of the transformative genetic potential (the Holy Grail) that is innate to the human genome.

Aether: ancient Greek name for the subspace field of Torsion Energy responsible for universal manifestation. Sometimes spelled "ether," this generative, conscious energy flows like time in a sacred geometric spiral that has been called phi, the Golden Mean, and the Fibonacci sequence. Modern scientists are returning to the notion of Aether using such phrases as Zero Point Energy. As this higher-dimensional light materializes in the creation of form, it becomes liquefied light or Plasma.

Age of Consciousness: dawning Aquarian "Age of Light" that many believe will soon precipitate the dissolution of old hierarchical structures of control, fear and manipulation, followed by the birth of social models based on principles of partnership, servant leadership, Unity Consciousness, and Unconditional Love.

Articulation (Bioenergy Enhancement): second DNA activation in the Regenetics Method. Appropriate as of the five-month mark of Potentiation Electromagnetic Repatterning, Articulation is designed to stimulate bioenergy or Kundalini and enhance creativity while facilitating the transformation of limiting thought-forms.

Atmic Permanent Atom: stable force center that is the soul portion of our being. Collectively, the Permanent Atoms serve as data memory banks for establishing the educational circumstances (Karma) of a given incarnation. In addition to the Atmic, the Permanent Atoms include the spiritual, emotional, mental and physical, which correspond to the four lesser Subtle Bodies. While these align with particular lower Auric Fields in dualistic pairs, the Atmic Permanent Atom that gives rise to the Soul Body remains unified in the Master or Source Field as the divine aspect of ourselves that never experiences fragmentation and loss of Unity Consciousness through Duality.

Atonement: often misunderstood term that can be read as "at-one-ment," or Healing into wholeness (Enlightenment) by returning to Unity Consciousness.

Aura: prismatic halo of bioenergy surrounding the human body composed of interconnected electromagnetic or Auric Fields. These fields provide an index of the relative health of the organism's underlying energetic structure. The Aura represents both a bioenergetic and Multidimensional blueprint.

Auric Field: one of a set of high-frequency electromagnetic bands composed of sound in higher-dimensional octaves, referred to collectively as the Aura and matching the Chakras in order and number. Each Auric Field, in tandem with the corresponding Chakra, governs a set of related functions in humans. Prior to Potentiation Electromagnetic Repatterning, most people have an unstable structure of nine Auric Fields (and Chakras) that initiate at the physical level and become increasingly "subtle." During Potentiation the Auric Fields and Chakras recalibrate from nine to an "infinity circuit" based on the alchemically transformative number 8 as the Fragmentary Body is transformed through Sealing.

Autoimmunity: degenerative condition often induced through genetic alteration (reverse Transcription) by invasive factors such as vaccines and genetically modified foods in which the immune system begins attacking the body's own toxic cells.

Biological Terrain: internal measure of microorganism levels in relation to one another. Biological Terrain, said to be balanced or imbalanced, is determined by such factors as stress, toxicity, antibiotics use, and vaccine history.

Biophoton Light Communication: data communication network used by living organisms essential to proper biological functioning and immune response that employs light to transmit and receive information. The cellular Hologram equivalent of the nervous system, the system of Biophoton Light Communication operates far more quickly than the nervous system and may be thought of as a parallel-processing "biocomputer" allowing for an unmediated energetic interface with the individual's environment.

Black Hole: region of space-time said to result from a collapsed supernova from which it was once thought not even light could escape. Recently, however, physicist Stephen Hawking admitted that Black Holes may leak information. Some theorize that as the Black Hole at Galactic Center becomes more energized, it catalyzes human evolution through Torsion Energy emissions transmitted via the Photon Band by way of the sun—an idea consistent with the ancient notion that Galactic Center is the womb or Source of life.

Black Road: ancient Mesoamerican name for the Multi- and Transdimensional "road" leading back to our ultimate "home" in Galactic Center (Source).

Chakra: bioenergy locus designed to process higher-dimensional light (Torsion Energy) in the form of a wheel found in the Subtle Bodies of humans. The Regenetics Method recognizes nine principal Chakras. Each of these corresponds numerically to an Auric Field and functions in tandem with it, such that the first or "root" Chakra aligns with the first field, the second or "sex" Chakra aligns with the second field, etc. The majority of elements governed by a particular Auric Field also apply to the corresponding Chakra. Together, the Chakras and Auric Fields establish the holographic interface that gives rise to the human form.

Child of Light: ancient Mesoamerican phrase for the next evolutionary stage of humanity set to occur in conjunction with the close of the Mayan calendar in 2011 or 2012. The Child of Light or Adam Kadmon inhabits a fully activated Lightbody and acts out of Unity Consciousness and Unconditional Love.

Clearing: term for energetic allergy treatment popularized by Dr. Devi Nambudripad, developer of NAET®. The term Clearing has also been applied to emotional release work. Sometimes used as a synonym for DNA Activation in the Regenetics Method.

Curing: act of alleviating a symptom or ailment in another person or in oneself without necessarily assisting the sufferer to achieve Healing.

Cymatics: study of the effect of sound waves on physical (including molecular) form.

Dark Matter: phrase recently coined by scientists to indicate the invisible ninety percent or more of the universe, which apparently resides in other dimensions. It has been theorized that Dark Matter, also referred to as the "space matrix" and "quantum potential," is Torsion Energy. Dark Matter is a way of conceptualizing the higher-dimensional light (often called "black light" in shamanic traditions) that becomes Plasma during physical manifestation.

Descension: alternative way to conceptualize ascension emphasizing that evolutionary transfiguration, rather than an earthly exit, can be a process of grounding the divine energy of the soul in physical form by creating the Soul Body or Lightbody.

DNA: deoxyribonucleic acid. Technically a salt (sodium) and thus an excellent conductor of electromagnetism, DNA is found principally in the nuclei and mitochondria of animal and plant cells, forming the genetic code in sixty-four three-letter combinations of Nucleotides called codons.

DNA Activation: electrogenetic mode of intercession capable of noninvasively stimulating a self-healing potential in the genome, specifically by stimulating rearrangement of Transposons in Potential DNA. The Regenetics Method employs three integrated DNA Activations. Sometimes referred to as Clearing.

DNA Phantom Effect: discovery made famous by the Gariaev group in Russia that wave-activated DNA is capable of communicating outside space-time by creating wormholes as channels for transmission and reception of universal creative consciousness or Torsion Energy.

Duality: divided state of being that has abandoned Unity Consciousness in favor of binary thinking and fragmentation. Duality also refers to the holographic system (the universe) birthed by this divided consciousness. In humans Duality imprints and sustains itself in the Fragmentary Body.

Electrogenetics: see Regenetics.

Electromagnetic Group: phrase coined by the developers of the Regenetics Method to indicate any of twelve family groups of humans sharing a unique bioenergy structure at the level of the Auric Fields and corresponding Chakras.

Elucidation (Triune Activation): third and final DNA Activation in the Regenetics Method designed to activate a mostly dormant portion of the neocortex, establishing the "ener-genetic" precondition—the Unified Consciousness Field—for Lightbody creation. Elucidation, appropriate following Articulation Bioenergy Enhancement as of the 42-week mark of Potentiation Electromagnetic Repatterning, encourages transcendence by assisting the individual to replace limiting and/or harmful emotions and beliefs with life-affirming ones.

Energized Narrative: phrase coined by the developers of the Regenetics Method to describe the particular combination of sound and intention (words) delivered in the form of higher-dimensional Spiral Standing Waves to initiate DNA Activation.

Enlightenment: process and result of allowing the light of soul in to the point that one becomes the light of soul. Genuine Enlightenment results from Healing or "wholing" through the embodiment of Unity Consciousness. By definition, Enlightenment involves creating a stable Lightbody.

Epigenetic: adjective used to describe Transdimensional self-organization functions observed at the level of Introns/Transposons in Potential DNA.

Exon: known coding segment of genes active during normal biochemical genetic replication involving RNA Transcription of DNA codes.

Fragmentary Body: name given to the second Auric Field and corresponding Chakra in humans. The Fragmentary Body is a "Frankenstein's monster" of energies, many of which do not belong in the body. The energy for parasites, for example, attaches to the second Auric Field and Chakra. The Fragmentary Body is an anti-Enlightenment "rift" in the human bioenergy fields that limits one's ability to embody Unity Consciousness. During Potentiation Electromagnetic Repatterning, the Fragmentary Body is transformed through Sealing, which represents a critical first step in bridging Duality at the biological level.

Frequency Domain: phrase coined by physicist David Bohm equivalent to dimension that indicates a certain frequency range of the electromagnetic spectrum. With each of the electromagnetic or Auric Fields occupying a particular Frequency Domain, the Aura can be said to contain the human Multidimensional blueprint. The Regenetics Method recognizes eight perceptible Frequency Domains that can be made to align through Potentiation Electromagnetic Repatterning with the numerically corresponding Auric Fields and Chakras.

Galactic Center: astrophysical name for Source located between the Black Hole and White Hole at the center of the Milky Way Galaxy. Also called Healing Sun and Tula.

Galactic Year: one of several cycles of time ending with the close of the Mayan calendar in 2011 or 2012. It takes 225 million Earth years for our galaxy to make one complete rotation through the Photon Band, which is believed to be a galactic "birth cycle." At the beginning of this cycle, Earth's landmass, Pangaea, began separating into the seven continents. This process of planetary Individuation correlates with continental drift theory.

Ge: name for the omnipotent creational "tone" of Unconditional Love, the primary Torsion Energy (conceptualized in the Regenetics Method as Silent Stillness) emanating from Galactic Center. This divine "frequency" promotes permanent Healing or Enlightenment by activating the Holy Grail (Lightbody) potential that lies dormant in Potential DNA. The name "Ge" most likely stems from the G-shape of the Milky Way Galaxy as it spirals outward from Source, during which Ge differentiates into helical waves of higher-dimensional sound and then light.

Genetic Sound-light Translation Mechanism: phrase coined by the developers of the Regenetics Method to indicate the process by which chromosomes assemble themselves into a solitonic lattice designed to "translate" stable Spiral Standing

Waves of sound (phonons) into light (photons), and vice versa. The conception of the human body as a Hologram depends on such a mechanism, which mirrors the cosmological model behind Regenetics in which sound becomes light during physical manifestation.

Golden Mean: phi ratio of 1.6180339 that serves as a cornerstone for sacred geometry, from the mathematics of the DNA molecule to the structure of the galaxy. Also known as Fibonacci sequence.

Green Language: musical vowel-only language of genetic transformation. Medieval alchemists used this phrase probably owing to the alteration of hydrogen bonds, which are green on the electromagnetic spectrum, in biological water molecules that occurs during Lightbody creation. Also called *lingua adamica* and Language of the Birds.

Healing: ultimately self-directed process leading to Enlightenment that involves transcending Duality by returning to Unity Consciousness, reuniting with Source as an individuated being, and becoming "whole."

Healing Sun: ancient Mesoamerican name for Galactic Center that highlights the restorative quality of the Torsion Energy manifesting as higher-dimensional light emitted by the Central Sun of Source.

Heisenberg Uncertainty Principle: discovery popularized in Quantum physics that a scientist always affects the outcome of an experiment simply by observing it.

High-spin Metal: one of six precious metals including gold, iridium, osmium, palladium, platinum and rhodium forming part of the human brain and central nervous system. This unique family of metals can be made to align their atomic spins by the six notes of the Solfeggio Scale combined with the Language of the Birds to stimulate an internal source of Torsion Energy called Kundalini that manifests as higher-dimensional light. The High-spin Metals are monatomically stimulated in Elucidation Triune Activation to facilitate Lightbody creation.

Hologram: illusion of form projected by intersecting electromagnetic waves. In a Hologram, the part always contains the whole (the modern way of saying "As above, so below"), everything is energy, and matter per se does not exist.

Holographic Model: phrase based on the theories of Richard Alan Miller, Karl Pribram, David Bohm and others that evokes the Hologram-like nature of reality. A holographic universe is composed of intersecting Spiral Standing Waves of sound and light that project the illusion of matter.

Holy Grail: genetic potential for Enlightenment or metamorphosis into the Lightbody that emerges when Potential DNA is keyed to create a crystalline, Merkabah-based "song grail" or "love song in the blood" in tune with Galactic Center's signature tone of Ge.

Hypercommunication: extrasensory communication similar to telepathy that transcends spatial and temporal limitations used, for example, in ant colonies. Also available to humans, Hypercommunication operates via the "biological Internet" of DNA. The Regenetics Method can be thought of as a practical application of Hypercommunication.

Individuation: process and result of separating from Source and achieving individual consciousness. After people individuate, it becomes possible for them to return to Source (Unity Consciousness) as fully realized individuals who have achieved Healing and Enlightenment.

Intron: apparently noncoding segment of genes and primary aspect (with Transposons) of Potential DNA. When Transcription enzymes have transcribed a gene, editing enzymes remove the Introns and splice together the known coding segments, called Exons.

Karma: law of the holographic multiverse designed to teach individuals responsibility for the full range of their creations.

Key of Life: device also known as an ankh featured in Egyptian hieroglyphics. The Key of Life may have been a type of actual tuning fork for harmonizing with Galactic Center's signature tone of Ge, or may have symbolized techniques (such as use of the Solfeggio Scale) for producing this celestial harmonization. In either case, the Key of Life is of a musical nature and designed to be employed with the Language of the Birds to stimulate Potential DNA to create the Lightbody.

Kinesiology: science of muscle testing. Kinesiology employs muscle-response (strong or weak) tests to determine allergies, emotional blockages, and even the truth or falsehood of given statements. Since its invention in the 1960s, kinesiology has become popular among both alternative and mainstream healthcare professionals.

Kundalini: human "life-wave" of Torsion Energy that lies mostly dormant in the second Auric Field and corresponding Chakra until activated. In Vedic teachings Kundalini is considered the highest evolutionary force capable of unfolding one's full bio-spiritual potential of Enlightenment when awakened. Following Sealing of the Fragmentary Body through Potentiation Electromagnetic Repatterning, Articulation Bioenergy Enhancement is designed to gently stimulate and integrate Kundalini starting at the genetic and cellular levels.

Language of the Birds: vowel-only phonetic language of a musical nature (see Solfeggio Scale) historically employed by master geneticists such as Jesus to activate Potential DNA to create the Holy Grail or Lightbody. Also called *lingua adamica* and Green Language.

Lightbody: divine physiology also known as the Adam Kadmon, the Child of Light and the Soul Body structured on the tripartite Tetrahedron shape and the Merkabah, designed to hold the full light of Unity Consciousness.

LOVEvolution™: term coined by Barry and Janae Weinhold to indicate that the driving force behind evolution is the primary Torsion Energy of Unconditional Love.

Master Field: name given by the developers of the Regenetics Method to the field where the highest of the five Subtle Bodies, the Soul Body, resides. The Master Field exists outside the Multidimensional (holographic) electromagnetic spectrum in a Transdimensional state of Silent Stillness (Unconditional Love) associated with the tone of Ge. Also called Source Field.

Meridian System: Eastern system of subtle energy lines in the human body that serves as a basis for acupuncture and acupressure, which typically recognize twelve principle Meridians.

Merkabah: "trinitized" vehicle of light based on interlocking Tetrahedron shapes resembling a three-dimensional Star of David that emerges from within the human form during Lightbody creation or Enlightenment.

Morphogenetic: adjective popularized by biologist Rupert Sheldrake to characterize the "ener-genetic" field constituted by DNA that connects all biological species regardless of time and distance.

Multidimensional: adjective used to indicate the multi-layered nature of reality beyond what the five senses can perceive in three-dimensionality. The human Auric Fields can be thought of as a geometric matrix that allows access to as many as eight increasingly subtle dimensions or Frequency Domains. This unfolding of perception to the full range represented by the electromagnetic fields and corresponding Chakras is what it means to become Multidimensional.

Nadi: one of a network of tiny tubular channels acting like "fiber-optic" extensions of the human nervous system that filter the Torsion Energy of Source through the Subtle Bodies. These channels, governed by the Auric Fields, pass to specific areas of the subtle anatomy via the Chakras.

Nonlocality: term derived from "nonlocal" employed by physicists to describe Newtonian logic-defying interactions between subatomic particles that take place at a distance.

Nucleotide: one of five combinations of a nucleic acid and a phosphoric group that form DNA and RNA used during creation and Transcription of genetic codes.

Ophiuchus: occulted thirteenth astrological sign, also known as the Serpent Bearer and located near Galactic Center, symbolizing DNA's role as a unifying network that links the other twelve astrological signs corresponding to the biblical Twelve Tribes, the twelve pairs of cranial nerves, Earth's twelve tectonic plates, and the twelve Electromagnetic Groups identified by the developers of the Regenetics Method.

Photon Band: higher-dimensional "life-wave" of Torsion Energy structured on the Golden Mean connecting Earth to Galactic Center via the sun that serves as a guiding data communication network for human and planetary evolution. Sometimes referred to as Photon Belt.

Plasma: matter in an electrified state that can be conceptualized as liquefied light, or the form light takes during physical manifestation.

Positronium: subatomic particle composed of a negatively charged electron and positively charged positron that illustrates how Lightbody activation occurs by resolving internal Duality. Since electrons and positrons are antiparticle opposites, after combining to form Positronium, they instantly cancel out each other and decay into two particles or Quanta of light.

Potential DNA: phrase coined by the developers of the Regenetics Method to replace "junk" DNA to denote the transformational potential that awaits activation in the human genome. Potential DNA interfaces with the "life-wave" of Torsion Energy emanating from Source responsible for giving rise to a particular physical form through RNA Transcription of DNA. This evolutionary activation occurs as Potential DNA's Transposons are consciously activated to rewrite or reprogram the genetic code.

Potentiation (Electromagnetic Repatterning): first DNA Activation in the Regenetics Method that initiates an electromagnetic repatterning designed to "reset" the human bioenergy fields at a higher harmonic resonance with Source. Potentiation also transforms the Fragmentary Body through a process called Sealing, initiating the Healing of Duality at the biological level.

Quantum: particle of light or other electromagnetic radiation. As an adjective Quantum refers to the science devoted to the study of subatomic phenomena.

Quantum Potential: phrase coined by physicist David Bohm to refer to the aspect of Nonlocality where space ceases to exist and two electrons, for example, can occupy the same coordinates.

Radionics: instrument-based form of energy medicine that has historically been performed at a distance.

Regenetics (Method): registered service mark for an integrated method of DNA Activation. Regenetics also describes a field that represents the exciting confluence of energy medicine and molecular biology. As such, it is a synonym for Wave-genetics and Electrogenetics.

Ribosome: tiny protein structure designed to carry messenger RNA (mRNA) containing DNA codes out of the cell nucleus during Transcription.

RNA: ribonucleic acid. RNA, in tandem with Ribosomes, is directly responsible for Transcription of DNA codes and protein synthesis.

Samskara: Vedic term describing an ingrained thought-form that maintains one's consciousness in a limited (unenlightened) state.

Scalar: term coined by Nikola Tesla to indicate thought or intention Torsion Energy capable of traveling faster than observable light. The Regenetics Method theorizes that Scalar waves are identical, for practical purposes, to prana, chi, orgone, Aether, and Kundalini—all of which are forms of Source energy that, after differentiating from the creational sound current of Ge, manifests as Spiral Standing Waves of higher-dimensional light.

Sealing: term employed by the developers of the Regenetics Method to indicate the stage of "ener-genetic" repatterning in Potentiation in which the bioenergy vacuum constituted by the

Fragmentary Body is closed. Sealing is a critical step on the path to genuine Healing and Enlightenment, as it lays the groundwork for a stable Lightbody by establishing an "infinity circuit" of eight Auric Fields and Chakras.

Silent Stillness: see Unconditional Love.

Solar-planetary Synchronism: phrase coined by Sergey Smelyakov to describe how Earth connects to Galactic Center via our solar system in a harmonic fashion based on phi or the Golden Mean. See Photon Band.

Solfeggio Scale: recently "rediscovered" six-note musical scale believed to contain the exact frequencies used by the Creator to fashion the cosmos in six days. Sacred chants such as the Gregorian once employed these notes to harmonize humanity with Source and increase vitality and longevity. Today's musical scales lack these six frequencies. One of the Solfeggio notes, "Mi," has been used as a frequency by genetic engineers to repair damaged DNA. This is also the principal note employed in Potentiation Electromagnetic Repatterning.

Somvarta: Vedic term for the powerful "life-wave" of Torsion Energy (universal creative consciousness) from Galactic Center responsible for the spontaneous evolution of species.

Soul Body: another name for the Lightbody.

Source: name for the Unified Consciousness Field of Unconditional Love between the Black Hole and White Hole at Galactic Center that uses the omnipotent tone of Ge to create and evolve life. Also known as Healing Sun and Tula.

Spiral Standing Wave: higher-dimensional Torsion Energy derived from the tone of Ge manifesting as sound and light (in that order) capable of stimulating rearrangement of

Transposons in Potential DNA outside space-time, simultaneously promoting Healing and Enlightenment.

Subtle Body: one of five energy bodies in humans denominated physical, emotional, mental, spiritual, and Soul. The first four of these are sometimes called the "lesser bodies." The Regenetics Method as a path of Healing through conscious personal mastery works through these bodies, from the physical to the mental to the emotional, until the spiritual body is activated by the individual to begin embodiment of the Soul Body during Enlightenment.

Superluminal: adjective used to describe anything that moves faster than observable light such as higher-dimensional Spiral Standing Waves of Torsion Energy.

Tachyon: one of a group of Superluminal particle-waves, the discovery of which has challenged many of the assumptions of traditional Quantum physics.

Torsion Energy: recently coined scientific term for universal creative consciousness or subspace energy (Aether) experiencing itself in time. In the galactic process of creation, the primary Torsion Energy of Unconditional Love differentiates into Spiral Standing Waves of higher-dimensional sound and light—in that order—forming a sacred trinity. Torsion Energy in the form of a "life-wave" (see Photon Band) interfacing with and modifying Potential DNA's Transposons is the driving force behind the evolution of human consciousness and physiology.

Transcription: biological "composition" process in which genetic codes are transferred from one kind of nucleic acid to another, especially from DNA to RNA. In the case of reverse Transcription, which often occurs as a result of vaccination and consuming genetically modified foods, RNA rescripts DNA.

Transcription is both a biochemically and electromagnetically driven process.

Transdimensional: adjective employed by the developers of the Regenetics Method to describe a unified state of being or Enlightenment, such as that achieved by those in harmonic identification with Source. Transdimensional refers to a state of Unity Consciousness and its corresponding Lightbody biology or "Triology" that transcend the Multidimensional nature of the holographic universe.

Transposition Burst: phrase coined by biochemist Colm Kelleher to describe a massive molecular rearrangement of Transposons in Potential DNA involving perhaps thousands of genes that occurs during genuine Enlightenment or Lightbody creation.

Transposon: term recently employed by cell biologists to describe what has also been called "jumping DNA"—tiny segments of Potential DNA that can be prompted by Torsion Energy or universal creative consciousness to change their positioning in the DNA molecule, rewriting or reprogramming the genetic code.

Triology: term coined by the developers of the Regenetics Method to indicate the evolutionary movement of human biology based on binarisms (Duality) toward a "trinitized" consciousness and corresponding physiology (the Lightbody) expressed in the Merkabah by way of the Tetrahedron shape.

Tula: ancient Mesoamerican name for Galactic Center or Source believed to be the true home of the god-man Quetzalcoatl. Also referred to as Healing Sun.

Unconditional Love: primary Torsion Energy of Source. Theorized in the Regenetics model to be Silent Stillness, the womblike nothingness between the Black Hole and White Hole at Galactic Center, Unconditional Love differentiates into higher-dimensional Spiral Standing Waves of sound and then light (forming a sacred trinity) during manifestation of form. Unconditional Love is the omnipotent creational potential driving, by way of the Photon Band, the evolution of human consciousness and physiology.

Unified Consciousness Field: phrase coined by the developers of the Regenetics Method to describe both Galactic Center and the "ener-genetic" precondition for Lightbody creation. When the individual's Auric Fields and corresponding Chakras have unified in a single gestalt that resonates throughout at Source's signature tone of Ge, manifestation of the Lightbody or Soul Body can occur. Elucidation Triune Activation, the third and final DNA Activation of the Regenetics Method, is designed to assist in the establishment of the Unified Consciousness Field.

Unity Consciousness: defining characteristic of the next evolutionary stage of human consciousness set to occur in conjunction with the end of the Mayan calendar in 2011 or 2012. Accessible at any time, Unity Consciousness has been called by many names, including Enlightenment as well as Christ, Buddhic and God consciousness. Unity Consciousness recognizes the divine nature of all things and is capable of evolving an enlightened biology in the form of the Lightbody.

Wave-genetics: see Regenetics.

White Hole: "yang" complement to a "yin" Black Hole theorized to be the procreative aspect of Galactic Center.

Zero Point Energy: phenomenon in which biological organisms use more energy than they can extract from their intake of food, water, and air. This occurs as the distance between two non-charged surfaces, such as water and a cell membrane, becomes negligible, dimensional coherence ("lasing") occurs and, by most indications, higher-dimensional Torsion Energy is drawn from the vacuum potential of the space matrix.

BIBLIOGRAPHY

Alexjander, Susan, "Music to the Ears: The Infrared Frequencies of DNA Bases" (*DNA Monthly*, September 2005)

Baerbel, *DNA* (Summary of the German book *Vernetzte Intelligenz* by Grazyna Fosar and Franz Bludorf) (http://www.home.planet.nl/~holtjo19/GB/DNA.html)

Bailey, Alice, *Initiation Human and Solar* (Lucis Publishing Co., 1997)

Blavatsky, Helena, *Isis Unveiled* (Theosophical University Press, 1976)

Bohm, David, *Wholeness and the Implicate Order* (Routledge, 2002)

Braden, Gregg, *Awakening to Zero Point: The Collective Initiation* (Radio Bookstore Press, 1997)
—*The Isaiah Effect: Decoding the Lost Science of Prayer and Prophecy* (Three Rivers Press, 2000)
—*The God Code: The Secret of Our Past, the Promise of Our Future* (Hay House, Inc., 2004)

Broe, Robert and Kerrie, *Absurd Medical Assumptions* (Tuberose Publishing, 1997)

Bryce, Sheradon, *Joy Riding the Universe: Snapshots of the Journey* (HomeWords Publishing, 1993)

Calleman, Carl Johan, *Solving the Greatest Mystery of Our Time: The Mayan Calendar* (Garev, 2001)

Carey, Ken, *Return of the Bird Tribes* (HarperSanFrancisco, 1991)

Champion, Joe, "Transdimensional Healing with the ADAM Technology" (*Nexus*, March-April 2004)

Chishima, Kikuo, *Revolution of Biology and Medicine* (Neo-Haematological Society Press, 1972)

Chopra, Deepak, *Ageless Body, Timeless Mind: The Quantum Alternative to Growing Old* (Harmony, 1995)

Clow, Barbara Hand, *The Pleiadian Agenda: A New Cosmology for the Age of Light* (Bear & Co., 1995)

Cutler, Ellen, *Winning the War against Immune Disorders and Allergies: A Drug Free Cure for Allergies* (Delmar Thomson Learning, 1998)

Dossey, Larry, *Healing Words* (HarperSanFrancisco, 1997)
—*Reinventing Medicine: Beyond Mind-body to a New Era of Healing* (HarperSanFrancisco, 1999)

Eisenstein, Charles, *The Ascent of Humanity* (2005) (http://www.ascentofhumanity.com)

Emoto, Masaru, *The Hidden Messages in Water* (Beyond Words Publishing, 2004)

English, John, *The Shift: An Awakening* (Dreamtime Publications, 2004)

Fosar, Grazyna and Bludorf, Franz, *Vernetzte Intelligenz* ("Networked Intelligence") (Currently unavailable in English. Visit the authors' website at http://www.fosar-bludorf.com.)

Free, Wynn with Wilcock, D., *The Reincarnation of Edgar Cayce?: Interdimensional Communication and Global Transformation* (Frog, Ltd., 2004)

Gardner, Laurence, *Genesis of the Grail Kings* (Fair Winds Press, 2002)

Garnett, Merrill, *First Pulse: A Personal Journey in Cancer Research* (First Pulse Projects, Inc., 1998)

Gerber, Richard, *Vibrational Medicine: New Choices for Healing Ourselves* (Bear & Co., 1988)

Gibbs, W. Wayt, "Genetics Beyond Genes" (*Scientific American*, November 2003)

Goldman, Jonathan, *Healing Sounds: The Power of Harmonics* (Healing Arts Press, 1992)

Gray, William, *The Talking Tree* (Weiser, 1977)

Grof, Stanislov, *The Holotropic Mind: The Three Levels of Human Consciousness and How They Shape Our Lives*, with Bennett, H. (HarperSanFrancisco, 1993)

Hawkins, David R., *Power vs. Force: The Hidden Determinants of Human Behavior* (Hay House, Inc., 1995)

Henry, William, *Godmaking: How Ancient Myths of DNA Reveal the Miracle Healing Power of Our Mystic Anatomy* (Scala Dei, 2000)

—*The Healing Sun Code: Rediscovering the Secret Science and Religion of the Galactic Core and the Rebirth of Earth in 2012* (Scala Dei, 2001)

Horowitz, Leonard G., *Emerging Viruses: AIDS & Ebola—Nature, Accident or Intentional?* (Tetrahedron, 1996)
—*Healing Codes for the Biological Apocalypse*, with Puleo, J. (Tetrahedron Publishing Group, 1999)
—*DNA: Pirates of the Sacred Spiral* (Tetrahedron, LLC, 2004)

Huggins, Hal, *It's All in Your Head: The Link Between Mercury Amalgams and Illness* (Avery Publishing Group, 1993)

Hunt, Valerie, *Infinite Mind: Science of the Human Vibrations of Consciousness* (Malibu Publishing Co., 1989)

Hurtak, J. J., *The Book of Knowledge: The Keys of Enoch* (Academy for Future Science, 1977)

Jahn, Robert G. and Dunne, Brenda, *Margins of Reality: The Role of Consciousness in the Physical World* (Harcourt Brace Jovanovich, 1987)

Jenkins, John Major, *Maya Cosmogenesis 2012* (Bear & Co., 1998)

Kelleher, Colm A., "Retrotransposons as Engines of Human Bodily Transformation" (*Journal of Scientific Exploration*, Spring 1999)

Lindsteadt, Stephen, "Frequency Fields at the Cellular Level" (*DNA Monthly*, November 2005)

Lipton, Bruce, *An Introduction to the Biology of Consciousness* (videotape) (CELL, 1995)

Marciniak, Barbara, *Bringers of the Dawn: Teachings from the Pleiadians* (Bear & Co., 1992)
—*Earth: Pleiadian Keys to the Living Library* (Bear & Co., 1995)
—*Path of Empowerment: Pleiadian Wisdom for a World in Chaos* (Inner Ocean Publishing, 2004)

McTaggart, Lynne, *The Field: The Quest for the Secret Force in the Universe* (Quill, 2003)

Miller, Neil Z., *Immunization: Theory vs. Reality* (New Atlantean Press, 1996)

Miller, Iona and Miller, Richard A., "From Helix to Hologram: An Ode on the Human Genome" (*Nexus*, September-October 2003; reprinted in *DNA Monthly*, October 2005)
—"The Universe Is Obsolete: A Gallery of Multiverse Theories" (*DNA Monthly*, July-August 2005)

Miller, Richard A. with Webb, B. and Dickson, D., "A Holographic Concept of Reality" (*Psychoenergetic Systems*, Vol. 1, 1975)

Motoyama, Hiroshi, *Theories of Chakras: Bridge to Higher Consciousness* (Quest, 1981)

Nambudripad, Devi, *Say Goodbye to Illness* (Delta Publishing Co., 1999)

Narby, Jeremy, *The Cosmic Serpent: DNA and the Origins of Knowledge* (Jeremy P. Tarcher/Putnam, 1998)

Pearce, Joseph C., *Evolution's End: Claiming the Potential of Our Intelligence* (HarperCollins, 1992)
—*The Biology of Transcendence: A Blueprint of the Human Spirit* (Inner Traditions, 2001)

Polich, Judith B., *Return of the Children of Light: Incan and Mayan Prophecies for a New World* (Bear & Co., 2001)

Pribram, Karl, *Languages of the Brain* (Prentice-Hall, Inc., 1971)

Radhoff, Ron (quoted in *New Science News*, Vol. III, No. 2, p. 7)

Rein, Glen, "Effect of Conscious Intention on Human DNA" (Proc.Internat.Forum on New Science, 1996)

Ruiz, Miguel, *Beyond Fear: A Toltec Guide to Freedom and Joy* (Council Oak Books, 1997)

Sheldrake, Rupert, *The Presence of the Past: Morphic Resonance and the Habits of Nature* (Inner Traditions, 1995)

Smelyakov, Sergey, "The Auric Time Scale and the Mayan Factor: Demography, Seismicity and History of Great Revelations in the Light of the Solar-planetary Synchronism" (Kharkov, 1999)

Tachí-Ren, Tashíra, *What Is Lightbody?* (New Leaf Distributing, 1990)

Talbot, Michael, *The Holographic Universe* (HarperPerennial, 1992)

Tansley, David V., *Radionics and the Subtle Anatomy of Man* (The C. W. Daniel Company Ltd., 1972)
—*Radionics: Interface with the Ether Fields* (The C. W. Daniel Company Ltd., 1975)

Tolle, Eckhart, *The Power of Now: A Guide to Spiritual Enlightenment* (New World Library, 1999)

Vonderplanitz, Aajonus, *We Want To Live* (Carnelian Bay Castle Press, LLC, 1997)

Weinhold, Barry K. and Janae B., "Preparing for the Shift" (multimedia presentation, 2004)
—"Finding the Holy Grail" (*Inner Tapestry*, December-January 2004)

White, John and Krippner, Stanley, *Future Science: Life Energies and the Physics of Paranormal Phenomena* (Anchor Books, 1977)

Wilcock, David, *The Divine Cosmos* (http://www.ascension2000.com/DivineCosmos)
—"The Ultimate Secret of the Mayan Calendar: An Imploding Cycle of Energy Increase, Culminating in 2012-2013 A.D." (http://www.scottmandelker.com/TGS/Science/ultisecr.html)

INDEX

ABOUT THE AUTHOR

Sol Luckman is co-founder of the Phoenix Center for Regenetics and editor of *DNA Monthly*. He is also a writer of fiction whose seriocomic novels (the *Beginner's Luke* Series) employ humor to focus attention on the primacy of consciousness and imagination in creating our reality. For information visit http://www.phoenixregenetics.org or http://www.potentiation.net.

Ordering Information

Sol Luckman's Book One on the Regenetics Method, *Conscious Healing*, can be ordered through your local bookstore or, even more conveniently, through our online Bookstore at http://www.phoenixregenetics.org.

Libraries and bookstores can order directly from Booklocker Publishing by visiting http://www.booklocker.com.

Conscious Healing is also available as an ebook at both websites listed above.

Forthcoming by Sol Luckman ... The perfect literary companion to *Conscious Healing*:

Beginner's Luke: Book I of the *Beginner's Luke* Series.

Who would you be if you could be anyone? go anywhere? do anything? Well, you can! Luke Soloman will show you how.

Luke is more than merely self-conscious. He is sui generis, literally believing himself into being. *Beginner's Luke* is the first novel in a series of madcap adventures that collectively make up the imaginary life of this lovably irreverent modern-day Walter Mitty.

While titillating in the rambunctious tradition of Henry Miller and Jack Kerouac, this extraordinary début equally impresses as a work of art. Luke's obsessions with self, satire and slapdash humor combine to highlight a surprisingly serious point: *consciousness creates*. The point is there is a point to living in the imagination—for only through it can we reinvent our world.

Visit our online Bookstore at http://www.phoenixregenetics.org for information today!